THE PHANTOM GOODS TRAIN

○ SILVER LINK RAILWAY ANTHOLOGIES ○

THE PHANTOM GOODS TRAIN

and other ghostly tales from the tracks

○ Barry Herbert ○

● CHILLERS, THRILLERS AND ECCENTRICS ●

from

The NOSTALGIA *Collection*

To my Mother
whose support was so vital

A Silver Link book
from
The NOSTALGIA *Collection*

© W. Barry Herbert 1989 and 2001

First published as *Railway Ghosts and Phantoms* by David & Charles in 1989
This edition first published 2001

British Library Cataloguing in Publication Data

ISBN 1 85794 099 7

Silver Link Publishing Ltd
The Trundle
Ringstead Road
Great Addington
Kettering
Northants NN14 4BW

Tel/Fax: 01536 330588
email: sales@nostalgiacollection.com
Website: www.nostalgiacollection.com

Printed and bound in Great Britain

Contents

Acknowledgements

My grateful thanks are due to all those who helped me, in many ways, to compile the material for this book. I would particularly like to thank: E. L. Anderson, Stuart Bailey, Mrs C. Barker, R. J. Barry, R. L. P. Belanger, James Blake, Mr P. Briggs, H. B. Brookes, H. Bunting, H. E. Caunt, P. S. Chapman, Collins Publishers, Mr G. Coverdale, P. Craddock, Derek Cross, John Daubney, A. Dixon, A. Dodsworth, D. Duke, Durham County Library, B. C. Essex, Mrs E. Fox, Peter Grant, Andrew Green (Fontana Books), J. Hallam, B. Hamilton, Peter Handford, Jack Hayden, Mr G. Heathcliffe, M. A. Houghton, Ted Hudson, P. Hussellbury, H. C. Johnston, Doris Jones-Baker, G. Knight, G. Leslie, J. J. Leslie, A. J. Ludlam, Tom McDevitte, John McDonald, I. McGill, J. McIlmurray, Rev D. K. McKenzie, J. Marshall, Nick Matthews, R. R. Mester, G. Nash, *The Observer* newspaper, The Oxford Mail Newspaper Ltd, Patrick Stephens Limited, PC 1405, Mr D. Pearson, E. W. Poulter, M. Pritchett, Peter Richardson, Mr R. Robinson (who gave legal advice when necessary), D. M. Ross, John Rothera, P. Screeton, C. Selway, E. A. Shaw, M. Squires, James Tomlinson, Peter Underwood (Fontana/Collins Books), David Walker, D. Walker and D. Reynolds, C. E. Whitehead, L. A. Whitehouse, B. J. Willey, D. Winn, Simon Winser, A. Withnall, R. J. Woodward, and all other sources of help, direct and indirect.

Thanks are also due to my friends and everyone else who gave advice and encouragement.

1
Find the lady

*L*ong train journeys are often very boring and tiresome, especially if you are on your own. The monotony is relieved somewhat if you have the opportunity to talk to a fellow traveller who feels the same about long train journeys, then you have something in common, if only moaning about the rigours of train travel. Sometimes, however, fellow passengers prefer to relax and do not wish to indulge in polite conversation; they may just want to read a newspaper or magazine.

Our story concerns a couple, Mr and Mrs Wishart, who in the autumn of 1945 had occasion to visit relatives in Newcastle. The Wisharts, who lived in North London, were not looking forward to the long train journey one little bit; being just after the war, the trains were run down, lacked essential maintenance and did not keep very good time, so the Wisharts regarded the prospect of the journey with considerable misgivings.

They had to catch the 10.30am train from King's Cross, and to their amazement they found few people in the usual queue. They had bought newspapers and magazines to read on the journey and when they found an empty compartment they settled down. The windows were fairly clean – well, you could see through them – the layer of dust on the woodwork was thinner than usual and the compartment was reasonably warm.

The train left King's Cross on time and the Wisharts began to read their newspapers. Not much conversation took place as they became absorbed in their reading; an occasional smile and a feeling of companionship was enough.

Then an application of the brakes slowed the clickety-click of the wheels on the rail joints, and Mr Wishart looked out of the window. They were running past a maze of sidings packed with every kind of rolling-stock, and the tall chimneys of brickworks dominated the skyline.

'I think this is Peterborough, dear,' he remarked.

His wife consulted her watch. 'On time too – that's good!'

The long train eased into Peterborough and the announcer called out the station name. A few people were waiting on the platform, and the station staff busied themselves with mail bags and other items of luggage and parcels. At last the guard blew his whistle.

The Wisharts were about to settle down to their reading once more when the corridor door slid open and an elderly lady eased her way into the compartment. The newcomer was wearing a striking black silk dress and black hat, which were very reminiscent of the Victorian age. She was carrying a wicker basket measuring 2 feet by 1 foot; it was white and to Mrs Wishart it was typical of the lady's attire. The lady smiled and sat down opposite the Wisharts, carefully placed the wicker basket on the seat next to her, then folded her arms and composed herself in relaxation.

The Wisharts resumed their reading, although Mrs Wishart kept glancing at the old lady. She could not help admiring her dress – it was so Victorian and really out of place in 1945. The motion of the train and the clickety-click of the wheels had a somewhat soporific effect on Mr Wishart and he found himself nodding off. No conversation took place between the three people from Peterborough to Grantham. Mr Wishart slept – in fact, he snored – but the old lady was silent, obviously completely composed.

At last the train pulled into Grantham and Mrs Wishart nudged her husband. 'Can you get us a cup of tea, love?' she asked. And in a whisper, looking at the old lady, 'Perhaps she would like one too.'

Mr Wishart opened the carriage door and asked a porter how long they had to wait and whether he had time to get a cup of tea. The porter glanced at his watch. 'If you hurry, sir.'

Mr Wishart hurried off to the refreshment room, was lucky

enough to be served straight away and with difficulty got back to the compartment just as the guard was blowing his whistle. The old lady took one of the paper cups of tea and murmured her thanks. The Wisharts read the remaining news in their papers and looked out of the window, but the old lady was still silent and motionless. They kept giving her a glance but her eyes were closed and she looked very serene and still.

Eventually Durham was reached and the long train drew into the ancient city. As the brakes came on and the flurry of activity again took in more passengers and luggage, the old lady stood up and moved to the door. Mr Wishart stood too and opened it for her, handing her the wicker basket, which seemed surprisingly light. The old lady stepped off the train on to the now deserted platform, turned and said, 'I wish you many happy years.'

Then, as Mr Wishart was about to say 'Thank you', to his surprise she vanished into thin air.

Mr Wishart could not believe it. He stepped down on to the platform and looked around, but there was nowhere that she could hide – as if she would! He darted about looking to satisfy his astonishment, but the old lady had melted away.

The guard blew his whistle, so Mr Wishart climbed back into the compartment and sat down.

'Where's she gone, dear?' asked his wife.

'I can't understand it – she just vanished,' he gasped. Then he noticed the third cup with some dregs of tea remaining in it. It hadn't been a dream. Had it?

2
The bright light

On the evening of 25 October 1919, John MacDonald spent a few hours with his friend Jim Jackson at Berryburn Croft in the hills of Dunphail, Morayshire. At about 11.30pm he left Berryburn on his bicycle and cycled the 3 miles to Bogney railway crossing where he could travel along the pathway beside the railway line.

The moon was so full that it was almost like daylight. He continued on his way until he came to the deep cutting just below Achanlochen where he lived with his grandmother. Then, before his very eyes appeared the brightest light he had ever seen. He got off his bicycle and stood for a while trying to discover the cause of the brilliance. Eventually, however, it faded until the only light that remained was the moonlight that bathed the hills in its natural glow.

The next morning John returned to the place where he had been mystified the previous night. He searched the area for clues, but could find no answer to the mystery. He told the foreman, Mr Calder, of his experience, and he, too, had seen the light on the line when he had been walking along the path late that night. He learned that several other people had shared the experience and were convinced that it was a sign, perhaps from the supernatural world.

No answer could be found to explain the mystery of the bright light and from that day John MacDonald never again walked along the trackbed from Dunphail to Dava.

That same stretch of railway line had been the subject of another mysterious happening a few years earlier. In December 1917, the ground covered by a thick, hard crust of snow, John MacDonald was returning home on the path beside the railway at about 8pm when there appeared high in the sky beside the Plough stars an engine and four trucks containing cattle. He could see the trucks moving and smoke coming from the engine. Mr Calder and John's Uncle Angus, who had a large farm at Kerrow in that area, also saw the ghostly train and could give no explanation, apart from the fact that a train of 40 cattle-filled trucks had burned at Dava station about 30 years earlier and all the cattle had died.

3
Dunster goods shed

The goods shed at Dunster, on the now re-awakened West Somerset Railway, is the subject of a ghostly presence. The phenomenon takes the shape of a black shadow that moves about in the dark corners of the old cavernous shed in a menacing way, startling anyone who happens to be in the area at the time.

Apparently a shunter was killed inside the shed many years ago and it is believed that it is his ghost that haunts the shed looking for his train. Few people who have witnessed the apparition are prepared to share their experience, so perhaps it is one story where it is best to let sleeping ghosts rest in peace.

4
London's railway ghosts

Bank

Rail workers at Bank tube station complain of a pungent smell normally associated with open graves; as a plague pit is believed to have been situated nearby, it could explain the unpleasant odour that pervades the air.

The ghost of Sarah Whitehead has been seen in the garden of the Bank of England. Sarah was the sister of an employee of the bank who was caught forging cheques in 1811; he was subsequently sentenced to death for what was then a major felony. Sarah's mind broke with distress and for the rest of her life she visited Bank station looking for her brother. Following her own sudden death she was buried in an old graveyard that was subsequently destroyed to form one of the entrances to the station.

Moorgate

During the winter of 1974-5 workmen employed on adapting the Great Northern & City tube tunnels for main-line working often saw a man dressed in blue overalls walking towards them in the tunnel at night. As he approached they were terrified to see that his face bore a look of indescribable horror; he then vanished into the tunnel wall. It is believed to have been the ghost of a maintenance worker who was killed by a train on that stretch of line.

After the Moorgate disaster of February 1975, some newspapers reported that the apparition may have caused the driver's lapse of concentration that led to the crash. On the other hand, the ghost may have been a premonition of the disaster.

Highgate High Level

This station, situated in a deep cutting with tunnels at each end, possesses an eerie atmosphere. During the early years of this century, a man is said to have walked into one of the tunnels in the path of an approaching train to commit suicide, and his ghost is reputed to haunt the place.

The station was completely rebuilt in 1941 for the Northern Line extension from Finsbury Park to Alexandra Palace-East Finchley. The work was never completed, however, and the extension was abandoned. The line was closed to passenger traffic in July 1954 and to freight in 1964, and was finally lifted in 1971 after six years of being used to tow empty tube trains to and from the Great Northern & City line.

The modern station buildings stand forlornly in the deserted cutting without tracks and almost hidden by foliage, giving an emotive, eerie atmosphere. People who have stood on the station have experienced the feeling that they are being watched, and others living near the closed line at Highgate and Crouch End claim to have heard sounds of trains at night.

Alexandra Palace

When Alexandra Palace was built in the 1860s, gypsies had an encampment on the hilltop where the building was located. They were evicted by the builders and subsequently put a curse on the building with the words 'May death and destruction befall this place and everything associated with it.'

Within a year of its opening, Alexandra Palace burned down. Although it was subsequently rebuilt, for most of its existence the palace was regarded as a 'white elephant', and when plans were coming to fruition concerning its revival it was burned down again in 1980.

Two railway lines were laid to serve the place: that to Palace Gates closed in 1963, while that to the palace itself closed in 1954 after it was so nearly linked to the Great Northern & City tube into Moorgate. Thus, both were doomed to failure. Could the gypsies' wrath have been responsible for the non-completion of the Northern Line's extension, and even for the Moorgate tube disaster?

Restored and reopened once more in 1988, the building is now an exhibition and leisure complex. But one can only surmise at its future fortunes. . .

Elephant & Castle

Elephant & Castle underground station used to be haunted by mysterious running footsteps, knockings, tappings, and a self-opening door. Mrs G. C. Watson of Herne Hill, travelling home late one night, was the only passenger on the platform and was impressed by the eerie silence of the station. She saw a porter coming towards her and mentioned to him how still and silent the old building was. The porter agreed and said that several ghosts frequented the station. He told her of several frightening experiences that he had witnessed and was not anxious to repeat.

On night shift he usually spent most of his duty in the porter's room with the door firmly closed, but to his horror on several occasions the door had swung open on its own. He had looked to see who had opened the door thinking that one of his mates was playing a practical joke on him, but there was nobody in sight. This strange occurrence happened several times without any rational explanation.

He also often heard tapping noises and the sound of running footsteps, but again no reason could be found to explain them. His mate, who worked the other shift, also heard the strange noises, but on investigation no reason was evident. The ghostly sounds were heard mostly on winter nights and footsteps were also heard on the stairway, which at the time was deserted.

A porter at Blackfriars, Mr Horton, refused to work night shifts at Elephant & Castle after one night's duties in the porter's room when he heard running footsteps. He also had the frightening experience of hearing footsteps halting outside the porter's room, then two taps sounding on the door. In terror he opened the door but the platform was empty.

On Saturday nights the station was locked up, but passers-by were still surprised to hear the sound of running footsteps.

Lewisham

A few years ago a British Rail bridge inspector who had been working on the St John's flyover was waiting for a bus at about 2am at Lewisham clock tower, some 100 yards from Lewisham station, when he heard someone calling for help. The voice seemed to be coming from the roof of the tall buildings around him and the person appeared to be trapped. The inspector telephoned the police and a patrol car soon arrived. The policeman, who also heard the voice, was not perturbed, however.

'No one is trapped there,' he reassured the inspector. 'People often hear voices calling for help. They are the people who were killed in the St John's train disaster in December 1957 and it is a well-known fact here that the phenomenon has been active since the crash.'

Ickenham

At 2am on 2 March 1951 a London Transport engineer working at the end of the down platform at Ickenham station, near Uxbridge, happened to see an incredible sight that he would never forget, for his eyes alighted on the ghost of a middle-aged woman wearing a red scarf and beckoning to him. She indicated that he should follow her down a staircase. At that moment he did not realise that she was a ghostly creature and prepared to follow her bidding. However, she suddenly vanished from sight when she reached the last step on the stairway. The engineer still did not realise that he had been following an apparition and continued to look around for her. When he had searched everywhere to no avail he realised that he had seen a ghost at first hand.

Several other railway workers have also seen this ghost. Apparently, the lady fell on a conductor rail many years ago and occasionally she returns to the station to the scene of her fatal accident.

Watford Tunnel

When the London & Birmingham Railway was constructing its line near Watford and was excavating the land to bore Watford Tunnel, they had to cut through part of a churchyard. Coffins were exposed and considerable embarrassment was felt by the contractors as they had no prime intention of disturbing the dead. Remains of the corpses fell on the workers who naturally felt both horrified and frightened by their unpleasant experience.

When the line and tunnel were completed, the trains ran without any problem until the occurrence of a phenomenon at the tunnel. Footplate crews found that every time they fired their locomotives in the tunnel they experienced a vicious blow-back from the firebox, with the result that several drivers and firemen were badly burned. An investigation showed that this incident always occurred when the engine was directly beneath the churchyard, and the train crews surmised that it was the dead taking their revenge on the railway for disturbing their eternal peace.

5
The dwarf

A husband and wife were travelling by train from Ipswich, and as they passed a church the lady became aware of a curious apparition that seemed to come up through the carriage floor. It was a dwarf-like man, dressed in peasant's clothing probably about two or three hundred years old. He was crouching and looked up at the church as the train passed by, then disappeared into the floor.

Her husband was not aware of the incident and she said nothing about it except to ask him the name of the place that they had just passed. He told her that it was called Haughley. She had only travelled over that stretch of line two or three times, but her husband, an engine driver, had worked trains over it many times. Later she asked him if he had experienced anything unusual on that line, but he said that he had not. He did not believe in ghosts and would not have believed what his wife had seen. For her, believing herself to be psychic, the apparition was unforgettable.

The lady had had another curious experience many years ago. Her husband came home from work at all hours so she always kept the back door unlocked for his return. One night at about 2am she was awakened by somebody telling her that she had locked the back door and her husband would not be able to get in. Although she was almost asleep, she had to make sure. In fact, she had absent-mindedly locked and bolted it. She undid the door, went back to bed and a few minutes later her husband came home.

He was working with Jimmy Knightall the day before the contents of a munitions train exploded. Jimmy had said to him, 'I have a feeling that I'm not going to live much longer.' The next day he was killed in the blast at Soham.

6

Ghosts of the North West

Waterfoot

The Railway Inn at Waterfoot, near Rochdale, is believed to be haunted by a tall lady dressed in grey who appears in a particular bedroom and walks through a partition wall. She is known as 'Jane' by the licencees and is blamed for interfering with bedclothes by pulling them completely off the bed. A bricked-up room has been associated with the ghostly occurrences, although there is nothing unusual or macabre in the room.

Mayfield

Although subsequently used as a parcels depot, for 20 years Mayfield station in Greater Manchester was a terminus and shunting yard. A dilapidated building of crumbling walls, rusty ironwork, cobwebs, broken roofs and decaying platforms, it was the ideal setting for a ghostly experience, especially on a wild winter's night.

Fred Jenks, the station foreman in its more active days, knew that a man had hanged himself in the electric indicator box and that a former station foreman had hanged himself in the station lavatory. Also, a night workman had opened the baggage hoist thinking that the lift was at his level and had fallen 50 feet to his death down the shaft. Fred heard footsteps on three occasions, passing the foreman's office and continuing towards the baggage hoist, but he never saw anyone on the deserted platform.

Porter Ted Dyson, a tall, tough man, said, 'I was sitting here alone when suddenly I felt a prickly feeling up my spine, then I heard the footsteps.' Shunter Charlie Movey also had a similar experience. At about 3 o'clock one morning he was about to go off duty and heard footsteps close behind him; about a fortnight later he heard them again. He flooded the platform with light to bolster his courage and looked everywhere, but could find no explanation for the mysterious events; the sound of the ghostly footsteps seemed to pass very close, then within seconds they ceased.

To this day no explanation has been found to solve the mystery of this strange sequence of events that has puzzled everyone who knows the old building and has worked in or around the station complex.

7
The cold man

The following story was told by a retired railwayman, and his experience occurred at around the turn of the century.

'I was driving the 8.30 train to the North and left King's Cross 4 minutes behind time. I can't tell you what it was, but I only felt nervousness once on an engine, and that was on the night I'm talking about.

Now, sir, I don't know nothing about ghosts or spirits or apparitions – call 'em what you like – but I'm ready to swear before any judge today that I saw something of the kind that night, and no amount of argument will change my belief.

It was just when we were passing through Hatfield Town – I would take my oath for all I am worth – that a man stepped from the platform to the footplate, just as easily as though we weren't travelling about 55mph. I can see his face and dress to this day. It was the saddest face I have ever seen.

The eyes seemed to look right through you and he was dressed all in black. I never felt so terrified in my life.

The curious thing is that Dick, my fireman, saw nothing at all. He coaled up for the hill by Welwyn just as natural as though all was fair sailing, and when I tried to shout to him, I felt a great lump in my throat and not a word could I speak.

I soon noticed that the stranger never went to any other part of the footplate except to the spot where I stood, and he even edged up so close to me that I went cold all over. My feet were like lumps of ice. I think I must have acted mechanically for I watched the man put his hand on the regulator. I put my hand on his and the touch of his hand was like ice, but I couldn't loosen his grip and before I realised it steam was being shut off and we were slowing down.

Dick, my fireman, must have thought I was mad. He had been up on the tender breaking up coal. He came down and craned his neck to see why we had shut off steam, and saw as I did that the distant signal was off and after that the home signal stood for line clear. You wouldn't believe it perhaps, but it is the gospel truth that though I knew the way was clear I felt compelled to stop the train, and stop her I did just outside Hitchin station.

For nothing, you say. Well, heaven alone knows how, but it proved to be for a great deal. There were two trucks across the main line and although the signals were off, the way was blocked, so that me and the passengers behind me wouldn't be living to tell the story if I hadn't been helped by the cold man who stepped into the cab and shut off steam.'

8
Barkston South signal box

One midsummer night in 1961 Peter Handford, the well-known railway sound recordist, intended to make some recordings on the East Coast Main Line in the Grantham area – the exact location was to depend on the weather. In the early evening he called at Grantham station to talk to an inspector he knew there and told him that he had decided to go to Barkston Junction and spend the night there. He asked the inspector for relevant information on possible traffic.

It was dusk when he arrived at Barkston. He parked the car and walked around to decide on the best position for his microphones and other equipment. The South signal box was in darkness, which did not surprise Mr Handford as he had been told at Grantham that it would be switched out from 10pm. What did surprise him was that the door was open, so he walked over to the box thinking that plans might have been changed or that he had been misinformed.

He went into the box and said good evening to the signalman who sat inside gazing out of the window with his back to him. The signalman was startled to see Mr Handford, who explained the purpose of his visit, showed him his permit and asked his opinion on traffic prospects for the night so far as steam workings were concerned. The signalman seemed strangely disinterested and uncommunicative and started to talk about a girl who had recently been murdered in nearby woods by a man who was still at large. This was a complete surprise because murders at that time were rare enough to be widely publicised, and Mr Handford had not heard of any such happening, especially in the Barkston area.

He did not stay in the box more than a few minutes. There seemed little point in doing so and he wanted to get his equipment set up as it was about 10.45pm and nearly dark. During a long night's recording he looked across at the signal box from time to time, but at no time was it lit up and all the signals under its control were permanently at clear.

By 5am he had to abandon recording because of wind and rain, so he packed up his equipment and prepared to leave. Before departing, however, he walked across to the South box and found it deserted with the door locked. Later in the morning, when Mr Handford called at Grantham station, he was again told that Barkston South box was unmanned during that midsummer night. Who then was the signalman?

9
The Hayling Island ghost

Mr S. Winser of Purbrook, Hampshire, recalls a newspaper article dated 30 October 1980 that told of the unexplained hauntings at the old disused Hayling Island station.

The branch was closed on 4 November 1963 after nearly 100 years of service. A quaint line, its train nicknamed the 'Hayling Billy', it was well used in early post-war years, but like many others it found that progress meant more cars and the forsaking of local branches, which in many cases were closed in the teeth of opposition from a new generation of travellers.

The service usually consisted of a Stroudley 'Terrier' 0-6-0 tank locomotive, a class originally used on several Southern branch lines and built in the late 1870s, yet still capable of running a service. The Hayling Island 'Terrier' usually hauled one non-corridor coach as this formation was considered adequate for the number of passengers using the service.

After closure of the branch line and attempts to erase every sign of the railway, all that remained was the goods shed and platform at the southern terminus. The local council once used the area as a storage yard for its vans and other equipment, but later the site became disused and abandoned, although the trackbed was used by horse-riders and walkers. The goods shed remained in surprisingly good condition, still displaying its Southern Railway paint, albeit rather faded now but still defiantly showing the old company flag.

As dereliction set in and the weeds strengthened their hold on the trackbed (one wonders why this attractive little line was not the subject of an attempt at private preservation), the 'Hayling Billy' became forgotten in the minds of many local people, but to some the memory lingered on in a very strange way.

In March 1969 a Havant Council workman and a Southern Electricity Board fitter were working in the old station on routine jobs when they encountered a ghost. One of these two gentlemen stated that he turned round to find a pair of legs behind him, but when he struggled to his feet the figure, wearing black boots and faded trousers, disappeared. Another council workman recalled that while he was working at a desk something grabbed his arm; he jumped to his feet, but there was nothing to be seen.

After their accounts appeared in a local newspaper, Mrs Elsie Taylor of Elm Grove, Hayling, claimed that the ghost was that of her late father, Jack Wilkinson, who had worked at the station for about 30 years. He had boasted that he would never die as long as the 'Hayling Billy' rolled along the tracks. In fact he died in 1947, but was apparently loath to leave the scene of his earthly toil.

Another strange incident at the station is recalled by Henry Cutting of Langstone. He was visiting his wife's parents in West Town and took a walk along the old line with his dog. Entering the station environs he wandered round the old crumbling buildings and eventually came to the little ticket office.

'I was thinking how wonderful it must have been in the old days when the old "Billy" was running,' he said.

He tugged at the lead but his dog would not enter the building. Its hair stood on end and it was plainly distressed. Mr Cutting had never seen his pet behave like this before and was very perplexed. He tugged again but the dog refused to move. Undeterred, he dropped the lead and entered the building alone to look around. Nothing untoward met his gaze except the usual scene of decay evident in an abandoned ticket office.

When he left the station and returned home, he told his father-in-law about his experience.

'No wonder,' the other man replied. 'That's the room the old station master died in. It was his office and they say he never left it.'

So the restless ghost of the station master still remains on duty and is perhaps happy in his old habitat doing nobody any harm. It is common knowledge that animals are more susceptible to paranormal phenomena than man, so we are left with an even stronger case for belief in this story.

10
The clairvoyant's warning

*M*any accidents involve interesting features that can be put down to human error, and it is very easy to be wise after the event, but the case of an accident at Barnetby, Lincolnshire, in 1983, when a diesel multiple unit (DMU) hit a Class 47 diesel locomotive hauling an oil train, remains, as the subsequent inquiry revealed, shrouded in an aura of mystery. The *Grimsby Evening Telegraph* reported the inquiry as follows.

'42799 IN FATAL ACCIDENT
The jinx that has haunted an Immingham-based Class 47 for over two years followed it to a remarkable crash at nearby Barnetby on 9 December.

After predictions of impending doom, BR even renumbered 47216 to 47299 in December 1981, but it obviously made little difference.

It was hauling an oil train when it collided head-on with a Cleethorpes-Sheffield Class 114 DMU . . . leaving one person dead, the diesel unit severely damaged, and both cabs of 47299 stove in.'

'A power cut to a signal box could have caused December's fatal rail accident at Wrawby Junction near Barnetby, a Doncaster inquiry was told yesterday.

One of the theories put forward for the crash between a two-car diesel multiple unit and an empty oil train was that a set of points had moved on their own, and a British Rail engineer said this could have been caused by a power cut. . .

The DMU was travelling from Cleethorpes to Sheffield while

the oil train was heading for the Lindsey Oil Terminal at Killingholme. Signalman Arthur Dennis Day who was on duty at the Wrawby Junction box at the time said that he noticed a "Track Failure" on one of the circuits. He advised the signalmen at their boxes on either side of him that he was going to crank the points manually, and went out with a flagman to do this.

After cranking them and checking that the points were lying correctly, he went back to his box. Then, after the oil train set off, the collision occurred.

Mr Day said he thought the accident happened because the points moved after he turned his back on them. He thought this might have been caused by the vibration of the oncoming oil train.

Another signalman, Mr Reginald Wilson, said he went off duty from the box before the accident and did not know anything about it until he was told by his son at 10pm. While on duty there had been no problem with the signalling equipment.

The driver of the passenger train, Mr Harold Faulkener, of Penistone, said he stopped at Wrawby Junction, where the signal was at danger, then received a hand signal to continue.

He had gone only a few yards when the accident occurred. Mr Faulkener told the inquiry that he saw the freight train on the opposite line, but at the time did not know if it was stationary or moving. The train was travelling at six or seven miles an hour, he said.

His guard, Mr Paul Anthony Vernon, said he was standing beside Mr Faulkener when the accident happened. He was trapped for some time with a girl passenger. The driver of the oil train, Mr Ambrose Thomas Kirman, said that at the junction he received a green hand signal to move forward and then, seeing a light ahead, sounded his horn. When he had increased speed, his engine veered to the right and the crash happened. It took him two or three minutes to release himself but he was not injured.

The Area Signals Engineer based at Grantham, Mr C. I. Weightman, said his inquiries had revealed that the integrity of the signalling system had not been brought into question. The circuit could have been reset by the public power supply to the signal box being interrupted. If there had been an interruption this could have affected the points.'

There is more to this story, however, than was revealed by this factual account. The freight engine was a Class 47, a reliable class of mixed traffic locomotives used all over the British Rail system. First introduced in 1962, these locomotives could handle any sort of working and were generally popular with the train crews. It is, nevertheless, possible for an unexplained jinx to attach itself to anything, and it would appear that something of this nature had affected this particular locomotive. It was said that 47216 had had more than its fair share of trouble, and concerns were being expressed on its availability.

Things happened to it that should never have happened. This trustworthy class of engines was usually renowned for its time-keeping, trouble-free running and ease of maintenance, but 47216 was said to be rogue. Although the faults experienced with the locomotive were easily overcome and explained rationally, it gained a bad reputation and was not welcome in some depots.

To add to the mystery, a clairvoyant telephoned a British Rail office and asked if they had a Class 47 locomotive. She was told that they had several hundred, and did she have one particular engine in mind. No 47216, came the reply, and the clairvoyant then warned that this locomotive would be involved in a fatal crash. This news was startling enough, but soon afterwards a warning letter was received at the same office.

British Rail officials were concerned and after some discussion they decided to re-number this errant engine 47299, perhaps wishing to rid the machine of its unsavoury reputation. For a while all was well and there were no further problems with the engine. However, the driver of the DMU waiting for the signal to proceed at Wrawby Junction one cold December day most likely did not know that the locomotive on the empty oil train was being hauled by the now disguised engine No 47216, running as No 47299.

Do point switches move on their own? What caused the power failure just at that crucial moment? Human error is always a possibility, but what forces were abroad that day that were to result in a fatal accident that fulfilled the clairvoyant's warning? Perhaps we shall never know, but it would seem that a tragedy was to happen whatever precaution was taken.

11
The mysterious intruder

The following story concerns two police officers who, while on their beat near the railway station in a little East Coast town some years ago, decided to check the coaching stock parked in the sidings overnight.

It was shortly after 2am on a moonlit September night. The two men had shared many duties together and on this occasion had just been to the police station for their refreshment before resuming their foot patrol. Passing the railway station, the two constables noticed a line of stationary coaches near Platform 1 and decided to check that they were not being used by intruders.

All was quiet as they clambered into an Open 2nd Class vehicle. They decided not to embark via the platform, but rather to effect entry further down the rake in order to surprise anyone who might be aboard. Once on board they quietly but thoroughly searched the eight carriages, checking that all doors and windows were tightly closed.

After satisfying themselves that all was safe and secure, they sat down in one of the coaches and decided to write up their notebooks. All was quiet and still, but suddenly the silence was broken by the sight and sound of the sliding door opening and shutting. The two men leapt to their feet, their powerful torches searching the dark corners of the coach. They again searched the rake of vehicles, even looking under seats, but no one was there. They also looked outside to see if there was a fugitive escaping under the bright moonlight.

They knew that they had both seen the sliding door opening and shutting and they were satisfied that when they had first sat in the carriage there was no one aboard. They were convinced that they were looking for a vagrant who had used the coaches for shelter, but they had conducted a thorough search and could find no answer to the mysterious intruder.

They examined the sliding door. It was somewhat stiff to move open and spring-loaded to close. Puzzled, the officers tried to form some logical conclusion. They again looked out of the windows on either side. All was still. Shining their torches, they carefully and quietly climbed down on to the ballast and looked on the underside of the vehicles. They re-boarded the coach and looked around again, totally bemused by the unexplained mystery.

They were not used to investigating the occult or paranormal, but when they re-examined the facts the thought occurred to them that they were dealing with an unseen presence. They had examined every inch of the coaches, had opened every lavatory door, looked under every seat. In other words, there was nowhere that a human being could hide from the probing torches, and they felt certain that no one had jumped off the coach. It was a mysterious event that appeared to have no explanation.

Fearing ridicule, the two policemen did not tell any of their colleagues about their strange experience. After much thought and consideration, no explanation was ever found, so no one will know whether the door was opened by a mysterious intruder or indeed a ghost.

12
Hauntings at Addiscombe carriage sheds

*T*he strange occurrences in the carriage sheds at Addiscombe in Surrey are well known to most of the staff, and the cleaners, shunters and signalmen who work through the night have many interesting stories to relate of their experiences.

The four-road shed is used to store and clean the electric multiple unit (EMU) stock used on Charing Cross and Cannon Street peak-hour suburban services, so the shed is only empty in the morning and evening peak hours.

At night the berthed electric stock is usually isolated by the shunter from the third rail electricity supply, and the hand-brakes are always screwed down tightly for safety reasons. However, on some nights the brake compressors are often heard running even though power to the units is cut when they enter the shed. On one particular night a cleaner heard the compressors of a train and told the shunter, who went and again cut the power to the train. Some time later exactly the same thing happened again, and the shunter again cut out this troublesome train, but it happened a third time and the man again cut the supply. This time all was quiet for the rest of the night.

Often during the night carriage doors are heard to open and close on their own, and the carriage cleaners' trolleys (with which they gain access to the train from ground level) are often moved during the night from where they have been left. These trolleys take some effort to move and make a considerable and distinctive noise, which on these strange occasions has never been heard.

One of the strangest phenomena to happen during the night is the definite rumbling sound of trains moving inside the shed, even when all are stationary. Indeed, it would be totally impossible for these trains to move as they are isolated from the power with their hand-brakes tightly screwed down. But strange as it might seem, all the signalmen have heard this strange, uncanny sound of a train moving out of the shed at night, and many have gone to the shed to see what is going on, only to find everything normal and still. One signalman was so worried about these sounds that he went to the shed and checked every hand-brake to find that each was fully wound down.

The shunters and cleaners have stories of their own. One evening a shunter and cleaner were sitting in the mess room having a cup of tea when the door, which was a tight fit, opened and closed. The two men got up quickly and tried to find who had opened the door, but there was nobody about at all.

An apparition was seen by a shunter when he was waiting outside the shed beside the platform sidings. When he saw a figure dressed in grey leave the sheds and walk along the track towards him, he was extremely frightened. When he saw that the figure's facial features were blurred and vague, he turned to get a better look, but the strange form suddenly disappeared. The shunter had the same experience in the evening, and drivers of incoming trains also reported seeing a figure standing beside the tracks outside the shed entrance staff door.

Although the shed has four roads, it is very unusual for any trains to be berthed in road No 4 as shunters and cleaners have reported that for some reason it is much colder by that road. Indeed, a shunter was crushed and killed between two units in the shed while coupling a train on No 4 road. Also a hot-water boiler had once exploded, killing some shed staff, and a driver, second man and blacksmith were killed when a train ran through the end of the shed, crashing into the smithy that was situated behind the building.

The shed was built in 1925 for the South Eastern Electrification Scheme, but nobody is sure how long it has been haunted. Mystery also surrounds the exact identity of the ghosts, although many people think that the main paranormal force is the ghost of the shunter killed in No 4 road.

All the above-mentioned details have been supplied by the signalmen at Addiscombe. Although many doubt the truth of the stories, there is too much corroboration to dismiss the strange tales out of hand. To date, no reasonable explanation has been forthcoming to dispel the long-standing ghost stories.

On one occasion a joke played on a trainee by a member of the platform staff and a signalman, who pretended to be a ghost, backfired in a strange way. The trainee was being instructed in the signal box and as part of his training he had to work at night for a week. One of the practical jokers was to hide in the shed and the other, after telling the trainee some ghost stories to frighten him, was to take him into the shed. They would then bang on the panels of the trains and open and close doors and generally make ghostly noises to frighten the newcomer as much as possible. The two men played ghosts for several nights until one night, as the trio passed the cleaner's lobby, the door handle rattled furiously of its own accord. Upon this, all three quickly left the shed for the signal box, suitably frightened. Obviously the Addiscombe carriage shed ghost wished to be included in their game.

13
The crossing of death

*T*he *Peterborough Citizen & Advertiser*'s headline for 1 March 1948 was 'Six German prisoners-of-war killed. Five injured as engine hits lorry in fog near Conington.' The report read as follows:

'Six German prisoners-of-war from Glatton Camp were killed and five more were injured when a light engine hit a three-ton lorry on this main-line crossing over the Peterborough-London line at Conington in dense fog at 7am yesterday [Monday]. Three were fatally injured and three more were killed instantly. The remaining five were admitted to Peterborough Hospital in a serious condition. They were travelling to work at Messrs B. & C. Papworth's Charter Farm, Speechley Farm and Darlow Farm. Visibility at the time was about 15 yards. A lorry that was carrying three of the injured men together with Dr T. Kuhlo and his medical orderly (both Germans) was in collision with an Eastern Counties bus on the narrow road not far from the scene of the accident. The doctor and the orderly were both badly injured and the bus and the lorry were badly damaged.'

The accident happened on a railway crossing with a reputation for narrow escapes, mainly caused by people's negligence in failing to close the gates securely and not being sufficiently observant when crossing the busy main line that carried high-speed traffic to and from London.

The crossing lies on a very narrow road and the gates in those days were opened by the road users. The railway company displayed warning notices in prominent positions near the crossing, but people nevertheless were careless and lives were lost.

The tragedy was compounded later that year by an accident on the same crossing that took the life of one of Peterborough's most prominent and well-respected inhabitants, Col A. H. Mellows. On 16 October 1948 the colonel and his friend, Mr A. F. Percival, were returning home at about 5.25pm after a day's shooting near Conington. The two friends were travelling in the colonel's large black Chrysler car, and on reaching Conington level crossing they got out of the car, went to the crossing gates and looked up and down the line. The colonel remarked to his friend, 'That's the 4pm from London'; there was a train standing on the south side of the crossing some 200 yards away obviously waiting for the signal to proceed northwards towards the crossing. They were the colonel's last words.

Mr Percival opened the gates and watched the car slowly cross the line. His impression was that while Colonel Mellows had been looking in one direction at this train he had failed to notice a fast express that was bearing down on him from the other direction. The train ploughed into the car and instantly killed the colonel and his dog. Colonel Mellows was buried with full civic honours and his faithful labrador was buried beside the fatal stretch of line.

In time stories arose of strange happenings at the crossing. More than 12 signalmen have experienced inexplicable events and some have refused to work the box. Mr D. Ellis, signalman at Conington from 1956 to 1958, remembered looking out from the remote box over the flat windswept fens and hearing the gates clanging to and fro when they were locked.

In a BBC interview in 1973 several signalmen gave accounts of a large black car that was seen drawing up to the crossing obviously waiting to cross the line. By the time the signalman had walked down to perform his duty, the car had vanished. Other signalmen had experienced the apparition of the phantom car and had heard the crunch of gravel as it approached the crossing. In broad daylight one man was able to define the mascot on the radiator, which seemed to be the figure of a lady. Colonel Mellows's car had such a mascot. Everything pointed to the fact that Colonel Mellows had returned to the scene of his tragic death.

Mr Norman Jinks, who had custody of the box for many years, used to take his dog for a walk near the crossing, but the animal was always very distressed whenever they passed the spot where Colonel Mellows's labrador was buried.

In the 1970s the signal box was removed as part of the Peterborough area signalling modernisation and the crossing is now controlled by remote-control television from the next box down the line at Holme. Of course the official explanation of the removal of Conington box and the choice of Holme to supervise several crossings in the area will have been based on technical considerations, but behind the scenes how much of that choice was based on the events at Conington?

Some 40 years after the event, the crossing is still regarded with fear at night because of the unexplained events, and only a few brave people will venture near the scene of the two terrible tragedies and the restless spirit of a well-loved member of the local community who seems determined to continue his journey over the busy main line. Today, as high-speed trains fly along the main line over the crossing, their passengers little realise that they are passing the scene of such tragic events.

14
The Utterby Halt mystery

Several years ago Mrs Hewitt and her late husband were staying in Louth with friends. Being strangers to the area, one Sunday they decided to go for a ride in their car and explore the local countryside between Louth and Grimsby. They set off on the low road between the marshes from Louth and were heading for home via Fulstow when they noticed a sign to Ludborough and Louth. Turning into what is locally known as Peartree Lane, they approached the railway crossing at Utterby Halt. Mr Hewitt remarked to his wife that he thought this was the old Grimsby-Peterborough line that ran through Louth and Boston; it was then a freight-only line, used some three times a week.

Then followed an extraordinary sequence of events. As soon as the front wheels of the Hewitts' car moved on to the crossing the car stopped. Mr Hewitt sighed and tried without success to re-start the engine. An eerie silence descended and in spite of his efforts the car would not start. Mrs Hewitt began to feel very frightened that they might be hit by a train, but before they could leave the vehicle a gust of wind hit it, shaking it violently, and there was a roaring sound as if a train had gone straight through it. The combination of the wind and the extraordinary sounds terrified the Hewitts who were virtual prisoners in their car.

Eventually the eerie silence returned and Mr Hewitt attempted to re-start the engine. To his amazement it started instantly and he drove off the crossing and stopped on the other side.

In a state of severe shock, the Hewitts got out of their car and looked around. The rusty track of the crossing was a bed of tangled weeds. The sturdy gates, paint flaking off the surface, were firmly closed against the railway. Set back a little was the crossing-keeper's cottage with its distinctive Great Northern Railway architecture. It somewhat reassured the frightened couple to find nothing unusual to explain their traumatic experience.

Mr Hewitt decided to go to the cottage ask for some possible explanation. He knocked on the back door, but to no avail; the place was locked up although there were signs of habitation.

Research by the author to find a possible explanation led to a news item in the *Louth Standard* concerning a ganger called John Edward Lancaster who had the misfortune to step out of the way of a fast freight train and into the path of a Cleethorpes-London express passenger train. The coroner's report stated that Mr Lancaster had been killed instantly.

Was this the incident that the Hewitts experienced? After all, they had felt the mighty gusts of wind and the terrifying roar so reminiscent of an express train passing at speed. Certainly the paranormal was at work in conjuring up the frightening event that so unnerved the couple.

The brief details of Mr Lancaster's fatal accident are as follows:

Fog was laying its dense blanket over the Ludborough area on that damp day in January 1953. It clung to the cutting just south of Ludborough station and visibility was down to between 6 and 12 yards depending on the terrain. Mr Lancaster was a length ganger and he had just completed his stretch of track and was walking back towards Ludborough on the sleeper ends. The fogman was out at Utterby Halt to warn any train of the level crossing, so the fog detonators would be in position. In these dense foggy conditions Mr Lancaster would have heard the noise of a freight train coming from Louth so he would instinctively step to one side to allow the freight to pass him. Unfortunately the rattling freight train would drown the sound of the Cleethorpes to London express hauled by a recently overhauled 'B1' 4-6-0 fresh out of the shops and running very silently; as the driver stated later he didn't see Mr Lancaster until he was almost on top of him, so nothing could stop this fatal accident.

It would therefore appear that this dreadful accident had

recurred in ghostly fashion, possibly to reassert its violent effect and prompt its memory to survive for eternity. Further research has failed to provide any other relevant incidents at Utterby Halt, apart from the story of a lady who was killed by a train in the 1920s when she stepped carelessly from behind a local train from which she had alighted, and the occasion when a broken-down milk-float was abandoned on the crossing and was smashed to pieces by a train, the driver escaping injury.

As for logical explanations, they are difficult to find, especially as the forces of the supernatural defy rational interpretation. The terrifying phenomenon experienced by the Hewitts at Utterby Halt refuses to dissipate with the passing years, preferring occasionally to replay the harrowing series of events that cost a man his life.

15
The Horwich phantom

*B*ill Morris, a young apprentice at the Lancashire & Yorkshire
Railway Works at Horwich at the beginning of this century,
had a strange experience on the works line. It began with an
invitation to a footplate ride on a new locomotive's maiden run
in recognition of his work.

Horwich Works was on a spur of about 4 miles from the main
line. One snowy winter's day the foreman asked Bill to join him
on the footplate of a new 0-6-0T. The cab contained inspectors,
boilersmiths, the foreman, and the duty driver and fireman. Bill
was to act as look-out when they drove back bunker-first.

On the return journey Bill saw a man walking in the track
about 300 yards ahead; he was walking towards Horwich and had
his back to the engine. Bill shouted to the driver to brake and the
driver responded quickly and sounded the whistle. The man
ignored the warning signals and walked on. So convinced was
the young apprentice that the engine had run over the man and
killed him that he stepped down from the locomotive after it
stopped and walked away.

However, before long he heard his name being shouted and a
great deal of laughter. Not only was there no sign of a body
beneath the train, but also no mark of footprints in the snow.

'Would you mind telling us how your friend can walk along
the sleepers in 4 inches of snow without leaving a single
footprint?' they asked sarcastically.

From that moment Bill was the object of ridicule both at the
works and in his social life. Before long the story of Bill and the
ghostly figure on the railway track spread around the town. The
young man was unable to tolerate the jeering to which he was

subjected, so left home and found work at the BMC car factory at Cowley.

Almost a year later he returned home and happened to relate his strange experience to a publican. He had hardly finished the story when the publican asked his wife to fetch an old leather-bound book that contained the tale of a man seen walking along the works line at Horwich in thick snow and who had been oblivious to a train's warning signal. That had been 50 years to the day before Bill himself had seen the apparition.

16
Dalgarven signal box

S ignal boxes are emotive places, and perhaps because of their often remote and lonely locations they become the ideal settings for ghostly phenomena.

The late Derek Cross, the well-known railway photographer and raconteur, discovered such a story concerning Dalgarven box, situated between Dalry and Kilwinning on the old Glasgow & South Western Railway main line. Dalgarven was an intermediate block post; there were no sidings or crossovers, but it served as a useful break in the section to help maintain the safe running of the line. The box was at the end of a farm track and was extremely primitive, having no electric light or water. The signalmen had to cross all four running lines and trudge down the muddy farm track to an outside tap for water.

One night in the middle of the First World War the night shift worker, on taking over the box, went to the farm to replenish his water supply. The high density of wartime traffic was such that crossing the line at any time was dangerous. On this occasion, unknown to the signalman who was crossing the line, a goods train had been let away from Kilwinning on the up slow line; it hit him and he was killed. As it was during the war, no significant inquiries were made, but the suspicion lingered that the signalman at Kilwinning had let the goods train out of his loop without 'putting it on the block'. However, such were the subsequent strange happenings at Dalgarven box that nobody would work it at night.

Being interested in the stories of the ghost, Mr Cross visited the site several times towards the end of the age of steam, when it was worked only on morning shifts. It was a relief man's job as nobody would take it regularly and locals would not visit the box even in daylight. On one occasion the relief worker asked Mr Cross if he had come to photograph the ghost. Another signalman said that he had seen the ghost on summer nights, and although it was harmless he did not enjoy the experience.

A legend grew up that the ghost was seen only before an accident, and following a crash at Dalry in the late 1940s, the signalman at Dalgarven swore that his attention had been distracted by a man walking across the track. The inquiry proved that nobody had walked across the track at the time in question, so the cause of the accident remained a mystery.

Dalgarven signal box has gone now and it is difficult to even see where it was situated, but the story of the ghostly signalman will remain for ever.

17
The Waverley Route:
atmospheres of evil

Some places are shrouded in an aura of dread or horror that defies any rational explanation, deterring researchers and those who would try to probe its secrets. Such a place is Shankend near Hawick, with its lonely derelict mansion and large weed-infested garden. In its heyday the mansion was an imposing house overlooking the scenic Waverley Route from Carlisle to Edinburgh as it followed the undulating Border countryside, the remoteness of its situation allowing superb views of the winding railway.

Derek Cross visited the mansion in 1951 as it was ideally situated to photograph the line. Knowing nothing about the place and its past, he decided to explore the terrain to find a spot to set up his camera. However, he experienced such a strong sense of evil in the place, even in the summer sunshine, that he was forced to pack up his equipment and leave.

Some time later he mentioned his experience to the late Bishop Eric Treacy, the doyen of railway photographers. To Derek Cross's surprise, the bishop stated that the place reeked of evil and he would never return there.

A schoolfriend of Mr Cross, a keen hill-walker, mentioned that a superb photograph could be taken on the hill above Shankend. When Derek Cross replied that he knew of the spot but would not wish to return there, his friend said that he had felt the same sense of evil. His dog, a bold bull terrier, had also become terrified when he was in the location.

Such was the consistency of people's experiences at Shankend that Derek Cross decided to investigate the mystery. Apparently, during the First World War the mansion and its grounds were taken over as a prison camp for German prisoners-of-war. Following an outbreak of typhoid or cholera, in which many of the prisoners died, their bodies were buried more or less where they fell. After the end of the war the estate was sold, but nobody stayed long and it finally fell into disrepair. When Mr Cross asked the locals to show him around the place, not one was prepared to venture near the site, even on a fine day. Such is the feeling of impending doom at Shankend that one's only desire is to leave the place and never return.

In April 1961, while making recordings on the Waverley Route, Peter Handford had spent the day on Whitrope summit, but had eventually abandoned attempts at recording because of the unfavourable direction of the wind. He decided to move down to Stobs to attempt recordings on the other side of the summit on the climb from Hawick.

It was nearly dark when he arrived at Stobs and set up his equipment in a previously selected position above a deep cutting on the Whitrope side of the station. By the time the first train had climbed up from Hawick through the station into the cutting and away towards Shankend, it was pitch dark. Mr Handford was disappointed with the recording as the sounds did not meet his expectations, but by then it was too dark and too late to make a change of location. Another train came by, but again the recording was unsatisfactory. It was by now nearly midnight. Another train was due and, listening through his headphones, Mr Handford was puzzled by inexplicably eerie sounds that seemed to come from a group of trees nearby, above the cutting.

He switched on the recorder to catch any distant sounds that would add atmosphere to those of the approaching train and the distant whistle of the engine, but all he heard were the eerie sounds, which seemed to be a faint moaning and chuckling coming from the trees. The expected train eventually arrived, but just as it approached, one channel of the recorder inexplicably failed, ruining the recording. For the next hour or two Mr Handford tried to rectify the fault in the chilly darkness, but as it proved impossible, he decided to wait until daylight and to get some sleep meanwhile.

In the morning, having rectified the recorder fault, he walked down towards the station to look for a new location. He decided that on the way he would take a look at the clump of trees from which the eerie sounds had drifted during the night. There was no sign of animal habitation, no sheep in the area, no birds' nests or birds to be seen in the trees. Having walked among the trees, he noticed a group of metal markers protruding from the ground; they recorded the names of German soldiers who were buried there after their deaths in the nearby prisoner-of-war camp.

In subsequent night-recording sessions, of which there were several on the Waverley Route, Peter Handford always took care to use a location in a clearing in the woods above Stobs station rather than return to that first location above the cutting.

18
The grey train

*W*e have already encountered John MacDonald earlier in this anthology. He lived all his 78 years in the Highlands, and this is another of his stories that defies explanation.

'It was the last day of 1921. I had been playing my melodeon at a concert at the Dunphail school, which was situated next to the railway line of the old Highland Railway. The school was about a mile south of Dunphail station. I was making my way home, walking on the track side (I knew that I was safe because the last train had long gone that night). It was in the early hours just after midnight on a beautiful moonlight night and although I had enjoyed myself that evening I was sober and happy. So I was singing and whistling without a care in the world.

Where I was at that moment many strange things have been seen during the hours of darkness on the railway line. This particular area between Dava and Dunphail seems to have a very mysterious aura about it and the local folk cannot explain their fear, but never take a chance in case some harm should befall them. Anyway, at this moment I felt a strange feeling of fear and the hairs on the back of my neck started to rise and I had a feeling that there was a train on the line.

Now, there shouldn't have been. The service trains had finished, and unless the Highland Railway had reason to send a special train at this hour, it remains a puzzle.

I felt this fear very strongly and I felt compelled to turn and look back along the line and to my horror there was a train coming full pelt towards me. Clouds of smoke pouring out of its chimney, hauling four brightly lit carriages but with nobody in them. Also nobody was on the footplate, but the glow of the fire lit up the controls very clearly.

I quickly scrambled up the embankment to get out of the way. Then I noticed that the train did not seem to be making contact with the track. It appeared to be about 2 feet or so above the rails, almost floating. It was very eerie and ethereal and I was dumbfounded, almost unable to believe what I had seen before my eyes. A feeling of terror overcame me as I watched the ghostly train float out of sight in a swirl of mist. I sat on the bank side unable to collect my thoughts. What had I witnessed? At last I was able to make my way home. I didn't tell anyone of what I had seen. I was too scared to talk even to my friends at that time.

Later, when I was married and living here with my wife and family, I set out one lovely summer morning on my bicycle to go to Dunphail to see my mother who was living alone in Bogney Farm House where I was born; my father had passed on and my mother wouldn't leave the old family home. I was pleased to find her fairly well but she told me that her sister, Mrs Robertson, who lived at Carnoch near Dunphail station, had been very poorly, so one night my mother had set out to walk down the railway line to visit her.

At about 11 o'clock mother had set off for home and when she was coming up the line about a mile from Bogney she had a terrible fright. She thought she heard a train coming up the line but she knew that there couldn't be a train at that time of night. But she felt compelled to look back over her shoulder, and sure enough there was the grey train coming up full steam ahead. She hurriedly climbed up the bank and sat down. She then witnessed with terror the phantom train in its awesome fullness – the smoke pouring out of the chimney, the empty deserted footplate, the fierce glow of the fire, and the brightly lit but empty carriages, all possibly 2 feet above the track. She agreed with me that it seemed to float. She was terrified and for a time could not move. After a while she was able to resume her journey home and lay down on the couch with her clothes still on, such was the shock to her nerves.

It was daylight when she came to and she was able to go to the door and look out over the line. Everything was calm and still. She looked at the clock. It was midday and she hurried to the door to wave to the driver of the midday train as it passed. The driver waved back and threw out a newspaper for her as he always did, and her little dog then ran to the railway and brought back the paper.

Mother was astonished when I told her that I had witnessed the grey train many years before. We talked about it in detail for hours, wondering what it could mean, and we were both convinced that something was going to happen on that line. [As if their thoughts were answered, an accident occurred soon after when a track foreman was run down and killed by a train.]

Now there is no railway. The track and almost every visible sign of a railway has gone, probably for ever, leaving the ghost or ghosts to indulge themselves without interference. But things were not finished yet because my sister Mary was also to experience the strange happenings on that stretch of line, but in a slightly different way. She was walking home on the line and was near Dunphail station when she had a strange feeling that something was going to happen, and it did. Some unknown force hit her in the back, hurling her to the ground. She was unable to get up for some time, but managed to crawl home in a very bad way. She was never the same jolly girl again. She was 16 years old then and she lived another 20 years but was not the same and was not happy, so the experience was to have its lasting effect on the people that were chosen to see it.'

19

Mysterious encounter at Pinmore

*I*n June 1966 Derek Cross decided to photograph the 'Paddy' – the Euston to Stranraer express – passing the recently closed station that had served the tiny village of Pinmore in Ayrshire. It had been a year since the old 'Port Road' to Stranraer had closed and London to Stranraer trains were diverted via Ayr and Girvan. The removal of the signal box at Pinmore made his photograph possible as it gave an unimpeded view of the subject.

Mr Cross had chosen the ideal spot for his photography some three days earlier and the picture he wanted could only be taken during the ten days around the longest day when the sun came through a gap in the hills. To explain the nature of the Stranraer line, the initial grade up to Pinmore Tunnel is 1 in 54 and runs for about 4 miles. The tunnel cuts through a saddle into the valley of the Stinchar River, so on a calm morning even a heavy southbound train on the bank could hardly be heard from the Pinmore side of the tunnel. The summit of this very steep grade is in the tunnel and once out of it engines could shut off to get their breath back.

The 'Paddy' was due to pass through Pinmore at 5am. Mr Cross walked to the signal box at Girvan and waited until the train was 'belled' off Kilkerran, which gave him sufficient time to drive to Pinmore. That particular morning, which was midsummer's eve, the train was 20 minutes late. Mr Cross drove to Pinmore, parked his car in the old goods yard of the deserted station and made his way towards the line. At that moment a girl aged about 16 walked up from one of the scattered houses in the village and stood in the same spot that he intended to use for his photography. He wished the girl good morning and mentioned that he intended to photograph the 'Paddy'. To his surprise, she did not reply but looked at him so vaguely that he assumed she had not heard him.

In due course, Mr Cross took the photograph for which he had come and the girl crossed the narrow road and watched the train drop down into the valley. Although Mr Cross was perturbed at this strange encounter, he decided that she must be a village girl who watched the train then returned home. On reflection, however, he became increasingly puzzled by the mysterious young lady. He had known that the train was running late, but how could she have known? Yet she had timed her appearance so exactly that it seemed as if she had been forewarned of the train's arrival. Even if she had heard the locomotive's whistle as it entered the tunnel, she would not have had time to reach bridge in time to meet Mr Cross as he parked his car in the goods yard.

Derek Cross had also intended to photograph the Glasgow to Stranraer goods train that followed the 'Paddy', but he felt so uneasy that he drove straight back to Girvan. He explained his reason for returning so hurriedly to the crew of the Stranraer goods train. The late Jimmy Irvine, one of the drivers, said, 'Och, ye've seen that lassie that threw herself under a train at Pinmore in 1939.'

Some time later Mr Cross learned more details about the tragic death of the girl. Shortly before the war she had committed suicide by throwing herself from the bridge into the path of a train. In 1939 fashions were similar to the 1960s vogue, which may explain why Mr Cross believed that the girl was real rather than an apparition. He was left with the distinct feeling that he had encountered someone from the spirit world on that early midsummer morning.

20
The disappearing passenger at Kirkhill

*W*hen dealing with the paranormal or supernatural, it is easy to look for rational explanations, but logical reasoning cannot always explain the strange events that occur in people's lives. James Tomlinson had a mysterious experience that defies rational explanation and he is resigned to the fact that he will never satisfactorily solve the enigma of the disappearing passenger.

Mr Tomlinson was a guard on an EMU on the electric railway system in the Glasgow area and the incident occurred in the mid-1970s. On about the last trip of the night shift, around dawn, the EMU on which he was working was approaching Kirkhill, the terminal of that particular service. On arrival at the station, Mr Tomlinson saw standing on the platform a man about 5ft 6in tall, wearing a dark coat and soft trilby hat and carrying a briefcase, obviously waiting to board the train for the return journey.

As the train halted Mr Tomlinson changed the train indicator on the EMU for its return journey, then turned to look down the platform. The passenger was nowhere to be seen. Mr Tomlinson became very anxious and looked for the passenger both on and under the train. He had completely disappeared. The driver had seen no one on the platform and neither had the booking office clerk. So the mystery remained: where had the man gone?

James Tomlinson could not and still does not believe that he imagined seeing the mysterious passenger. Although he was subjected to ridicule by his colleagues, he remained firmly convinced. His only explanation is that possibly the gentleman had travelled on the line for many years in the past and that his ghost fitted into a well-worn slot in time. So was the ghostly passenger preparing to embark on another train journey as he had done many times during his life on earth? We shall never know, and James Tomlinson remains mystified by his strange experience.

21
A trick of the light?

The following story concerns the sighting of 'Deltic' locomotive No 55020 *Nimbus* entering Hadley Wood South Tunnel, even though the locomotive had been cut up seven months previously. The story was written by an observer and appeared in *Deltic Deadline*, issue No 17.

'When the day's main force has been spent, and the sun is sinking slowly beyond Penzance, the twilight comes to the confines of Hadley Woods. That strange zone of time and light between day and night is broken only by bats wheeling and diving across the expanse of the East Coast Main Line. Somewhere a dog howls. An up local slows to a halt at the signals on the edge of the woods. Everything seems as it should be. The moon is beginning to take the twilight, temperature drops alarmingly, there's a real chill in the air. In the distance comes the familiar note of a 'Deltic' engine but there's nothing scheduled. It's a bonus for the late train-spotter. Out from the New Barnet footbridge comes the 'Deltic', the throb of the Napier engines very reassuring, it seems. However, somehow different, somehow surrounded by a glow, an aura, perhaps a trick of the light.

While the local train gets the road and moves off, the 'Deltic' moves on, the familiar engines making the exhaust stand up into the dusk sky. Nothing can be wrong, surely? As it passes I turn and watch it enter Hadley Wood South Tunnel.

I shout to my friend, 'Did you get the number?'

'55020,' comes the reply.

'Yes, that's what I thought.'

For a few silent moments this doesn't click into place. Then we suddenly realise what we've said. But *Nimbus* was cut up seven months ago.

At Hadley Wood station we are told that no southbound train has passed through. A trick of the light?'

One can perhaps understand a spectral steam locomotive appearing wreathed in smoke and steam to fascinate the unsuspecting person, seemingly so solid that one could reach out and touch it, but a 'Deltic'? Here is a new dimension to the paranormal, the sound of diesel engines coming from a locomotive that appeared long after it had been scrapped.

It should be remembered that the East Coast Main Line was the regular haunt of the 'Deltics' all their working lives, so it is not surprising that one of their number should reappear on its familiar route.

For the record, No 55020 *Nimbus* was taken into service on 2 December 1962 and named the same day. It was withdrawn on 18 December 1979 and cut up at Doncaster on 2 February 1980.

22
Winsor Hill Tunnel

*I*n the early summer of 1956 Peter Handford was in the process of preparing to record traffic on the Somerset & Dorset line. He went first to Winsor Hill Tunnel, situated in a lonely spot approached by a climb over a viaduct from Shepton Mallet. The chosen location was on the Shepton Mallet side of the tunnel, where he intended to record trains approaching the climb. The tunnel, a short one, consisted of two single bores as the up and down lines were separated there.

As always, when deciding on recording locations, Mr Handford reconnoitred the surrounding area. On the far side of the tunnel, near the side of the line towards Bath, there was an immensely deep rock quarry, disused and deserted but containing some old equipment rusting away at the bottom. The whole area had a horribly uneasy and melancholy atmosphere and Mr Handford noticed that from time to time on that bright summer's day metallic rattlings came from the depths of the quarry. The sounds were inexplicable since the wind was blowing from the Glastonbury direction and the high ground shielded the quarry from it; the stunted bushes on the lip of the quarry were not moving.

The strange metallic noises continued at intervals whenever Mr Handford was in a position to hear them. Although he had intended to return to the Bath side of the tunnel at night to make recordings of the several trains that at that time ran from the north towards Bournemouth in the early hours of Saturday morning, he did not do so, partly because he was reluctant to visit the place in darkness and also because each time he visited Winsor Hill Tunnel to make recordings he experienced problems and misfortunes of one sort or another.

On the first occasion a violent thunderstorm blew up on that beautiful summer day, wrecking any attempt at further recording and causing damage to the equipment. On other occasions a wind suddenly blew from a direction that made recording trains on the climb from Shepton Mallet impossible, or a sudden rain storm blew up at an inopportune moment. Worst of all, perhaps, on a day of perfect weather conditions the recording equipment suffered an inexplicable fault that was impossible to rectify on location, so the whole trip was wasted.

Years later, when Peter Handford met the photographer Derek Cross, they discussed the Somerset & Dorset line. Quite unprompted, Mr Cross related his experience of the place, which tallied precisely with Peter Handford's, especially with regard to the disused quarry on the Bath side of Winsor Hill Tunnel.

23
The ghost of Darlington
North Road station

*T*he following story was published in the *Darlington &*
Stockton Times on 9 January 1960.

'More than a century ago the nightwatchman at North Road
station had a ghastly experience. This was before the North
Road bridge was built, and the Stockton & Darlington Railway
line passed over the Great North Road by a level crossing. Mr
James Durham, the nightwatchman, had a cabin near the
crossing and his beat was from the old goods station, east of the
crossing, to the passenger station on the west. One winter's night
about midnight, after his first perambulations, Durham went to
the porter's cellar at the station to have supper. The cellar had
been originally part of a railwayman's house and was provided
with a fireplace and a gas jet; it also gave access to a coal cellar.

Descending the stone steps from the station platform, Durham
turned up the gas and had just sat down on the bench and opened
his bait tin when he was startled by the apparition of a strange
man followed by a large black retriever dog emerging from the
coal cellar.

Realising that his visitor was no ordinary mortal, the
watchman did not challenge him but, jumping to his feet, he
kept his eyes fixed firmly on the intruder, hoping thereby to
induce him to retire. He noticed that the ghost was smartly
dressed in a cut-away coat with gilt buttons, a stand-up collar and
Scotch cap.

Walking towards the fire the ghost raised his hand and struck the watchman a smart blow on the body, which produced a strange sensation. Mustering all the courage he possessed the watchman assumed a defiant attitude and dealt the ghost a straight right blow to the body.

Durham's hand went right through the apparition and struck the fireplace, bruising his knuckles. The ghost shrieked out and fell backwards to the wall, whereupon the dog rushed forward and seized Durham's leg. Although, as he explained afterwards, Durham experienced a sense of pain, an examination of the skin revealed no mark or puncture. The ghost, having regained its upright position, called the dog by a click of his tongue and the intruders retreated into the coal cellar.

Taking his lantern the watchman followed and although there was no other entrance but from the porter's room, he could find no trace of his antagonists.

The railway ghost caused a great stir in Darlington at the time but many were very sceptical about its bona fides. The excitement was intensified when it became known that some time previously a railway clerk named Winter, who kept a black retriever, had shot himself in the porter's cellar, but Durham had claimed that he was unaware of the tragedy when he had encountered the ghost.

Many people questioned the watchman as to his condition on the night of the incident. One of them was Edward Pease [one of the original promoters of the S&DR], who invited Durham to his home and asked him many questions. Had he been asleep at the time? Was he subject to nightmares? Had he been drinking? Durham maintained that he was a teetotaller, his mind was free of trouble at that time, and that he had all his faculties.

The Rev Henry Kendal, Minister of Union Street Congregational Church from 1859 to 1893, testified to Durham's straightforwardness. Durham was a regular attender at Mr Kendal's church and he was regarded as a strong, reliable man whose word could be trusted.

Some time after, in 1882, the Society for Psychical Research was founded, and Mr Kendal sent details of the North Road station incident to the President, Prof Sidgwick, who asked for further details of Durham's bodily state on the eventful night. It was pointed out that he was a regular watchman who slept during the day so as to be able to perform his nightly duties. He had only been in the cellar for about one minute when the ghost appeared and he had had no time to doze.

In 1891 the Society conducted a 'Census of Hallucinations' throughout the country and Mr W. T. Stead, the journalist, assisted by enclosing some 100,000 census papers in the *Review of Reviews*, which he edited. This magazine published the story of the Darlington railway ghost as one of the most thrilling of a series of ghostly anecdotes.

Mr Kendal inspected the cellar in 1891 and found the place exactly as it had been when Durham used it. A few days ago I went warily – in broad daylight – down the steps to examine the cellar. The whole room, part of larger premises, is now used for coal storage, but the salient features of the story, the fireplace and coal recess, are in situ and it was not difficult to reconstruct the strange winter scene of over four generations ago.

James Durham died on 7 January 1917 aged 75, and I recently stood by his grave in the North Cemetery. The ghost fighter has now reached that blessed state "Where the wicked cease from troubling and the weary are at rest".'

24
The boy at Entwhistle Halt

*M*r D. K. McKenzie remembers a chilling story told by his uncle, Tom Ackroyd, who, from the time he left school in 1925, worked for the railway.

In 1935 Ackroyd was put in charge of Entwhistle Halt on the Darwen-Bolton line in Lancashire. There was nothing special about the halt: it had a signal cabin with about a dozen levers, and a pair of gates to allow carts to cross to the farms scattered across the moors. Apart from the occasional passenger, the main traffic was milk churns en route to the dairy, and dye wagons from Preston. The sidings were situated about half a mile away and there was a water tower nearby. Ackroyd enjoyed a quiet bachelor life and lived in a small house by the crossing.

Ackroyd's strange experience began one day as he looked out from his lonely signal box. He knew most of the men who used the line and passed the time of day with them. However, there was one person he saw frequently, but he never spoke to him, nor even knew his name. He first noticed the young boy early one summer, about a year or so after he had taken over Entwhistle Halt. One Saturday at about 3 o'clock, when the 2.47 had not long gone and he had put the 'line clear' through, he was standing at the window and saw the lad. He was no more than eight or nine, playing in the meadow on the far side of the up line to Darwen. He was running, just as children of that age do, almost as if he was chasing the shadows across the moor. At first Ackroyd thought nothing about it, but he saw him again the following Saturday at about the same time.

All through the summer he ran about in the meadow, chasing the shadows. The sheep were obviously used to him, for they never moved much for him. He came so often afterwards that Ackroyd began to look out for him when Saturday came round. He was a thin lad, dressed in dark short trousers and a grey pullover. Although he did not appear to be under-nourished, he was pale-faced. After a while, Ackroyd thought that he belonged to one of the local farms, and that because of his pale complexion he was recovering from an illness. The young boy did not appear after about September, but as the winters were so severe on the moors Ackroyd was not surprised.

During the summer months of the war years, Ackroyd watched the boy playing in the meadow beside the line. One year, towards the end of spring, he saw him earlier than usual, and saw him several times standing close beside the crossing gates on the up side, his face almost pressing between the bars. In an inexplicable way, the lad looked a pathetic sight. His little pale face always looked pinched and very sad. He stood at the gates evening after evening, but was always gone when the 5.13 to Blackburn went through.

One Saturday, late in June, in the last year of the war, Ackroyd passed the 5.13 through as usual, received the 5.29 from Chorley, and saw it in. Normally, he let it away at 5.43, but on that particular Saturday it was a minute or so late. It was 5.33 when he received 'train entering section' and 5.48 when he cleared the signal and heard the train start away.

Suddenly, however, he heard a lot of confused noises – the brakes screeched, steam hissed, and people were screaming and shouting. Ackroyd put the signals to danger, rang the station down the line to tell them that he had a problem, then rang the previous station to alert them that he still had the train in his section. All this he did before he even knew what had happened. When he had time to take account of the situation, it transpired that Bill Oldenshaw had fallen under the train at the crossing and been killed outright. The driver had not even seen him.

At about 8 o'clock there was a knock on Ackroyd's door. He opened it and found the line foreman standing on his doorstep.

'Now, then, Tom Ackroyd,' he said.

'Ow do,' replied the signalman.

'It's a bad business is this, Tom,' said the foreman. 'That were Bill Oldenshaw, him as has the farm over by Stones Place. That's the second from the family that's gone same way.'

'Nay,' said Ackroyd. 'I've been here some time now and it's never happened before.'

'No, well,' said the foreman, 'that last one were a long time before your time, Tom. I reckon it were about the time of the Great War. It were Bill's older brother. Bill were not more than a baby when his brother Harold died. Oh aye, I remember hearing that tale when I first joined. I were no more than a lad myself. Harold was about eight or nine and he was always playing and running about in that meadow yonder.'

Ackroyd knew immediately where he meant and his blood ran cold as he knew what the foreman was going to say next.

'Aye, he used to look out for his dad's cart on a Saturday at about 4.45 and he'd wait for it to come across the line there. Anyway, this Saturday he was late, no one knew why, and Harold just stood with his face against there waiting. Then he must have seen his father and the cart because the next thing anyone knew, he was through that gate and across – and that's when he went right under the 5.29.'

25
The Appleby Hall oak chest

Some years ago, when the locomotive shed was closed at Keadby, Lincolnshire, and engine power was concentrated at Frodingham, a pump-house was built beside the line there to supply water to the new locomotive depot. This pump-house was fully automatic and the latest example of technological design. It required servicing approximately once a month and usually three electricians from Scunthorpe carried out the work. The most convenient time for this routine servicing was on a Sunday, and the three men soon became familiar with the sophisticated equipment.

One Sunday, when the three men had finished their lunch break, they decided to walk across the scrubland adjacent to the main railway line. The weather was fine and they were enjoying their walk when they came across the neglected remains of a large house, which they had often seen in the distance from the pump-house. After viewing the outside and the wild, overgrown garden, they decided to explore the crumbling interior. It was a sad sight, with the faded grandeur of a once noble family home. The interior had been vandalised and parts of the house were obviously unsafe. The men moved about cautiously, looking with curiosity at what they might find. Suddenly, under a pile of wood, rubble and plaster, they found an old wooden box in remarkably good condition. After examining it, they considered that it would make a good tool-box and decided to take it with them.

On examining their find more closely at the pump-house, they found that the box was of stout construction and very old. The inside of the lid bore a faint inscription, which the men could not read. They decided to leave the box in the pump-house until their next visit.

Thereafter strange events took place. Inexplicably, the usually reliable pumps started to malfunction and finally broke down. And one of the electricians, a seemingly healthy man, was suddenly taken ill and rushed to hospital with a suspected heart attack.

One of the men then read an article in the *Grimsby Evening Telegraph* about Appleby Hall. Apparently, an old oak chest had been part of the family's possessions for generations and bore an inscription inside the lid that said something to the effect of 'Whoever removes this chest from Appleby Hall, ill luck will befall them'. Realising the cause of the inexplicable events that had recently occurred, the electrician telephoned the police. Subsequently the box was collected from the pump-house and returned to its place among the ruins of Appleby Hall.

The sick electrician made a remarkable recovery and the pumps resumed their efficient, reliable operation, but the strange experiences no doubt left an indelible mark on the memories of the three electricians who would never forget the malevolent power of that old wooden box.

26
'Humphrey' of Normanby Park

Normanby Park steel works and rolling mills were, in their heyday, one of the most successful processors of steel in the world, and provided employment for thousands of people in and around the Scunthorpe area. Like any vast industrial complex, it had its own substantial railway sidings to accept and move train loads of iron ore and to ship the completed products to its customers worldwide. However, despite its established position in the industrial world, the works had a frequent visitor from another plane, a ghostly figure known as 'Humphrey'.

It was believed that Humphrey was a farm worker employed on the Normanby Park estate in the distant past and that he had been found guilty of stealing from his employers. Apparently, he was beaten to death and, as a result, swore that he would forever haunt the local area. If the legend is true, he kept his word for he was seen on countless occasions over the years. In the shape of a little old man, bent and stooping with a bag on his shoulder, he appeared and disappeared at whim, often through walls and machinery, and terrifying anyone who saw him. He frightened train crews who saw him walking aimlessly on the railway tracks as if he were a real person.

One night a works policeman was disturbed in his office by a tramp-like figure wearing a strange hat. The policeman turned and spoke to the man and asked him what he wanted. However, the intruder refused to reply and disappeared through a wall. This incident so affected the policeman that he suffered a nervous breakdown from which, it is said, he never fully recovered.

Much to the consternation of the operators, Humphrey's

shabby figure would appear then disappear into high-speed machinery. One young man, who was attending a large machine that was railed off as a safety precaution, warned Humphrey of the dangers of moving machinery. The ghost, however, paid no heed, walked through the machine and disappeared through a wall.

It seems that Humphrey had several favourite places where he viewed the progress of the works, one such place being between the weighbridge and the steel works. One of the works engine drivers had a traumatic experience when he saw the old tramp pass straight through the train of works wagons as he was moving them. The shocked driver assumed that he had run over and killed someone on the line, but on investigation no one was to be found.

One day after dusk a weighbridge office employee reported seeing a tramp-like figure walk into his office, look around, then walk through the back wall.

Humphrey did not confine his activities solely to the steel works, but also walked across the fields he had known during his earthly days. One old lady recalls her days as a midwife many years ago when on one occasion she had to deliver a baby in an old farm cottage near the works. As she prepared to mount her bicycle to return home after the delivery, the proud father called out, 'If you see Humphrey, don't be frightened, he is quite harmless.' When she learned who Humphrey was, she only visited the cottage in daylight.

The train crew of a Class 31 diesel locomotive leaving Normanby Park sidings with a train of empty iron ore hoppers, en route to Immingham docks, had an unnerving experience. As the train approached the main line, the locomotive's second man drew the driver's attention to the shadowy figure of a tramp walking along the line in front of them. The driver braked hard and sounded the horn, but the man ignored the warning and disappeared under the train. Fearing the worst, the crew got off the locomotive and examined the train and the lineside, but could find nothing untoward. When the guard learned what had happened, he simply laughed and said that it must have been old Humphrey.

27
The Elsham phantom train

Not far from Appleby and Normanby Park is Elsham, where rumours of a ghostly train that appeared in foggy conditions near Ancholme Bridge on the line between Elsham and Worlaby led Ted Smith and Jack Brookes, two reliable men in their mid-50s, to investigate the tales and discover the truth for themselves. Both men were sceptical about ghosts and the supernatural and the aim of their jaunt in suitably foggy conditions was to return to their friends, who believed the stories, and good-humouredly disprove them. Not for one moment did the two men believe that they would see anything, and they were determined not to allow the foggy weather to affect their imaginations.

As the light of that winter day faded and the swirling fog closed in, the two friends took shelter in a platelayer's cabin at the northern end of a long curve in the line. Before long their confidence changed to an icy fear as they discerned through the enveloping fog the shape of a railway engine lit up by an eerie glowing aura. They were able to make out the locomotive's smokebox and cab, and the glare of the fire reflecting through the spectacle plate on the cab front. Knowing that it was basic railway practice to use detonators in foggy conditions to protect the signals, and that the sound they emitted carried some distance, the men awaited the series of bangs that would herald the presence of the train and confirm that it belonged to this world.

'It's a bit strange, isn't it?' said Jack.

Ted nodded. 'Doesn't look right to me, and it doesn't seem to be getting any nearer.'

'Surely the fog signals are out,' said Jack. 'Hope it's not that ghost train they keep talking about.'

Both men laughed nervously, neither sure of the truth.

'Tell you what,' said Ted. 'Let's go and see if we can see the "fogs", then when we're sure about them, perhaps we can get a close look at the engine – perhaps it's broken down.'

Jack agreed and they set off down the track, treading carefully in case they tripped over a signal wire. Reassuring themselves that the train had indeed broken down, both men felt confident that they would find nothing untoward on the line. Soon, however, they found themselves in a waking nightmare, for although they were walking towards the train they seemed to get no nearer to it. They could see the train, but it was enveloped in a haze or a glowing flame. The two men continued walking, trying to fathom the mystery of the fog-bound train.

'Just a minute, Ted,' said Jack. 'There's something strange going on and we're not getting any nearer, and look – there's some fog detonators clamped on the rail.'

Ted frowned and shivered. The fog was getting acrid now. Both men cleared their throats. The haze still surrounded the distant locomotive and train, discernible but somehow blurred.

'Come on, Jack, let's go home. I don't like this at all.'

Ted readily agreed. He was feeling the clammy cold that was penetrating his thick coat and chilling his bones. The two men groped their way back to the cabin, occasionally glancing back to see what had happened to the strange engine.

As they neared the hut they both stopped and looked back. They could not believe their eyes – the train appeared to be following them. They could still not clearly discern the engine in detail, for the haze still surrounded it, but without doubt it was following them and had passed over several fog detonators without setting them off. Terror gripped the two men as they ran as fast as they could away from the ghostly train towards Elsham signal box. They burst in on the somewhat startled signalman who was puzzled by the dramatic appearance of the two familiar faces.

Ted sank down with relief into a chair. 'Harry,' he gasped, 'there's a strange train on the line coming this way and it has run through all the "fogs" without setting them off.'

'Get away with you,' replied Harry. 'I've no train on the line. What are you talking about? just to satisfy you I'll ring Ancholme Junction box and see if the signalman knows anything about it. If there had been a train on his section, he would have offered it to me.'

Using his telegraph instrument he communicated with his colleague. No train had been past him and his fogs were out. Harry was convinced that he could account for every train he had accepted.

Their spirits revived by a cup of hot tea, the two men took their leave of the signalman. By now the fog had lifted, but it was so dark that it would have been futile to return to the scene of the mysterious train to discover for themselves any clues as to its reality or otherwise.

Jack and Ted kept their unusual experience to themselves, fearing the ridicule of their friends. It was not until several years later that they were able to unravel the possible cause of the visitation. One evening, in their local pub, the Dog & Rabbit, they met an old gentleman who had moved out of the district on retirement, but had returned to visit his daughter who still lived there. The old man loved to reminisce and would talk for hours about the past; he was a veritable fund of knowledge. Ted and Jack were drawn into conversation with him, and Ted, remembering the mysterious incident, asked him if he could bring to mind any relevant details. The old man's eyes lit up.

'Yes,' he said. 'I can tell you all about that. It were in the 1920s and it was a passenger train from Cleethorpes to Doncaster and the driver, well, he was a hard, fast driver and he wasn't popular with firemen. This particular day he had a young fireman called Tom Smith, a big strong lad with a fiery temper. The driver, Fred King, used to goad his firemen, always at them, never left them alone, so instead of getting the best out of them he seemed to be determined to get the worst instead.

'This particular day Tom Smith had been out on the drink the previous night and now had a sore head and a filthy mood on him. King was pushing him hard, telling him he was no good and such like, when to King's surprise Smith started to answer back, and no one ever did that, so things worsened and it wasn't long before they started fighting, an alarming situation on a small cramped footplate. It is believed that one of them moved the regulator and opened it up with the result that the train was soon out of control. Then reverse curves were coming up and the train ran through the first curve but was going too fast for the next one and it left the track, killing certainly the driver and fireman and one or two passengers, I believe. A very sad occurrence, and such violence. They say that the accident haunts those curves especially in dense fogs, but you'll not worry about that, it's probably an old wives' tale. Anyway, who'll have another drink? It's my round.'

28
The ghost of Bradley Fold West

*T*he signal box at Bradley Fold West, situated between Bolton and Bury in Lancashire, was a small but important location miles from anywhere, controlling up and down main lines and two goods loops. It had a crossover, a set of catch points and four telegraph block instruments, two for 'permissive block' working along the loops and the other two for 'absolute block' for the main lines. The control exercised from this remote box was vital to the smooth operation of this busy line.

Jack Rothera, an ex-Navy man, had wished from his boyhood days to work on the railway. After his demobilisation he was accepted by the railway authorities to train as a signalman. His first training began at Bradley Fold West and he soon realised that absolute concentration and alertness were essential qualities for the job. One slip or lapse and a terrible accident would never be far away.

Jack enjoyed his early training and displayed the sort of ability much sought after by the Signal & Telegraph Department. Johnnie Warburton used to work turn-about with him and they enjoyed each other's company. Johnnie also excelled at the job and progressed at the same rate as his friend.

Jack well remembers his first shift on his own. He had let a light engine out of the down loop ready to go to Bolton and had refused the bell code for a fast down freight from Bradley Fold Station box. He was just telling the driver of the light engine that he would be away in a minute, when from the Station box came the 4-5-5 bell signal – 'Train or vehicles running away in right direction'. As the heavy freight train rushed towards his box, the next box down the line at Rose Hill Junction accepted the light engine. Telling the driver to accelerate, Jack was able to stop the freight train without accident.

Following training, life for Jack soon settled into an interesting routine and nothing untoward happened to disturb the smooth operation of his signal box. Johnnie Warburton renewed his acquaintance with Jack when they were rostered to work alternate shifts. It was a happy working relationship and each had complete trust in the other's abilities – until Johnnie's happy-go-lucky character changed to an unusually quiet and sombre mood. Before long, Johnnie vowed that he would leave the signal box for ever.

Jack was puzzled at Johnnie's sudden change in behaviour, but he reasoned that his colleague must be troubled with a domestic problem. But why had he said that he would leave the box for good? Jack himself was very happy at Bradley Fold West and he had settled into the routine and managed the duties without any problems. What could have upset Johnnie? Jack speculated that perhaps there had been some interference by a superior, or that vandals may have seen the lonely outpost as a target for their attentions. Jack had himself experienced broken windows and other similar nuisances, but nothing more. After much thought and reasoning, Jack could reach no satisfactory conclusion regarding Johnnie's unhappiness. Nevertheless, he was not prepared to take chances, so he checked and rechecked the security of the box and the store-room below in case vandals from a nearby village might be intending to pay him an unwelcome visit.

A few days later Jack took over the shift at 9pm. At 1.47am he received the bell signal from Rose Hill Junction asking if the line was clear for the 2am 'target', an express parcels and newspaper train. As all was clear, Jack turned the block over to 'Line clear'. Some 2½ minutes later he received the bell code indicating that the train was entering his section. He turned the block over to 'Train on line', warned it on to Bradley Fold Station and pulled his signals off.

The train could now be heard coming up the bank. It was going like the wind, as it always did, and in seconds it had passed the box exactly on time. Returning his signals to danger and sending the 'Train out of section' to Rose Hill Junction, Jack prepared to book the train's passage in the train register book. As he did so, he heard footsteps passing under the bridge, over the wooden boarding covering the point rods and continuing under the box. Remembering Johnnie, Jack concluded that a prowler had come in search of the coal that was stored in bags under the box. Grabbing his torch, he raced down the steps and shone the light into the dark corners, but there was no one to be seen.

The strange occurrence was uppermost in Jack's mind the following night and he determined to catch the intruder if he returned. As on the previous night, the mail train roared past the signal box at the usual time and Jack again heard footsteps walking under the box in the still night. Taking a heavy poker in one hand and a torch in the other, he charged down the steps, feeling certain that the intruder had entered the store-room, but as before no one was there. Feeling frightened, he scurried back up the stairs and sank bewildered into his armchair. He was convinced that the uninvited visitor was a light-fingered local looking for free coal; the thought that he might be dealing with a supernatural force did not enter his mind.

Next day Jack pondered the mystery of the unexplained footsteps and laid plans to catch the intruder. But as he commenced the night shift he felt an inexplicably sinister atmosphere. He felt edgy, but convinced himself that his nerves were playing tricks on him. Then he heard strange clicking noises at the windows and footsteps coming up the steps. Flinging open the door, he shone his torch, but nothing stirred. Returning to his chair, he sat and waited.

Now he heard a low whistling sound that seemed to come from the rear of the box. With his poker and torch he sought out the noise, but again found nothing.

An hour later he opened the door and shone his torch again. Although the fresh night air was welcome, Jack was again aware of an unusual feeling of dread and foreboding. He had never been afraid or apprehensive before, but now he realised that something was amiss. He closed the door and opened the sliding window in the front of the box looking across the tracks. The clear moonlight showed the gleaming metals of the line. Looking right then left he saw the signals with their warning lights reassuring him of their presence. Suddenly he felt that he was being watched. Turning round quickly he saw a shadow moving across the ceiling light. He pinched himself and shuddered against the extremes of the cold night air and the warmth of the signal box. Warming his hands on the fire, he wondered about the shadow and the feeling of being watched. He was looking forward to the end of his shift.

As the mail train thundered past and disappeared into the distance he heard the familiar sound of footsteps. Rushing down the staircase, he turned the corner to the store-room, which was fitted with a safety lock requiring four turns of the key. Nobody was there, but the air was heavy with a sense of foreboding. Then an agonising cry rent the still night. Jack hastened to the front of the box, shining his torch across the tracks. To his horror, he discerned a recumbent shape at the side of the line. He ran towards it fearing the worst, but to his amazement the figure faded and disappeared as he neared the lineside. Baffled and frightened, Jack now understood the significance of Johnnie Warburton's change of mood. But what was the agonised cry and the figure lying by the lineside? Had someone been killed by the mail train? The footsteps, the mysterious whistling noises, the shadows and the figure by the track – why had he been witness to these events? In a state of nervous confusion, Jack was unable to answer these bewildering questions.

Numb and shivering, he walked slowly back up the stairs. Huddled by the fire he waited impatiently for daylight and his relief. By now he was determined to relinquish his night-shift duties; the thought of undergoing such traumatic experiences again was unthinkable.

Years later Jack was told that some time before his tenure of Bradley Fold West signal box a man from a nearby village had been killed on the line. According to reliable sources, but unknown to Jack, at least three other signalmen had experienced the same chain of events, but all had kept their frightening experiences to themselves to avoid the ridicule of their workmates.

29
The ghostly caretaker

Jack Cartwright, his wife June and their two children, 11-year-old Alan and 13-year-old Melissa, had been on a camping holiday in the West Country, but unfortunately everything had gone wrong. The weather had been appalling and as a result the whole family had caught colds. Their misery was complete when one night vandals had visited their camp site and caused considerable damage, including slitting the Cartwrights' tent. When the electrics on their normally reliable car had started to fail, Jack and June had decided to cut short their holiday and return to their home in South Yorkshire.

Packing up their equipment, they set off. Darkness began to descend quickly as rain-filled clouds turned the sky to a menacing black void. Before long the family ran into a ferocious thunderstorm. Driving with difficulty through torrential rain while thunder and lightning crashed overhead, Jack found himself in a narrow West Country lane, and realised that he had missed the turning that would have brought them back to the main road. By now it was dark, they were obviously lost and their headlights were beginning to fail. Their only hope was to find a farmhouse where a friendly farmer might be able to offer them shelter for the night.

As they began to despair, Alan noticed a railway station sign. Peering through the pouring rain, Jack saw a post with an old weather-stained sign hanging from it. They drove towards their refuge and soon found themselves in a large station yard, overgrown with weeds and bramble bushes; like so many abandoned branch-line properties, the dereliction was complete.

The storm had now passed its zenith and although the rain was still pouring down, the Cartwright family felt relieved at finding some form of shelter. Jack drove the car as near as he could towards the station building and switched off the faltering engine. He took a torch, left the car and examined the old building. After what seemed an age, he reappeared from the gloom and got back into the car.

'I've had a good look round, June,' he said. 'The roof seems sound and I think I can force one of the windows and get in. It's a bit of a mess but at least we can be warm and dry in our sleeping-bags.'

When they reached the building, Jack shone his torch through a broken window, illuminating the interior of what had evidently been the booking office. The floor was covered with the rubbish of years, but the place seemed dry and the family's spirits rose. Jack prised open the rotting window with a screwdriver, and the family moved in everything they needed to make their stay as comfortable as possible. June lit their camping lamp, which cast weird shadows around the room.

After a meal, Jack suggested a walk to explore their surroundings. They found a long platform and the remains of a goods shed. The trackbed was weed-ridden and strewn with rubbish, and a sense of complete abandonment overhung the once proud station. Picking their way through the rubble, the Cartwrights concluded their exploration, although they had no idea of where they were.

As the children walked ahead, Jack and his wife agreed that they could sense a strange atmosphere, something eerie and unpleasant. The children then ran back excitedly to them.

'There's a light in one of the rooms and we've heard voices,' said Melissa.

Their father told them that as they were the only people present in the deserted station, it was not possible to have seen or heard such things. The children, however, were persistent and led the way round to the side of the building, stopping at what had probably been a small parcels office. Peering through the filthy window, they saw an empty room littered with rubble, several dust-covered pieces of broken chairs and an old table, but no sign of life. Jack looked at the children.

'But this is the place, Dad,' said Melissa. 'There was a light like an old oil lamp giving a yellow glow, and we heard voices, too.'

Jack believed that they could not be imagining it.

'I know,' he said. 'Let's see if we can get in from the inside, as this door is either seized up or securely locked.'

Jack climbed back into the booking office, fetched his torch and screwdriver and made his way carefully to the door that would give entry to the parcels office, shining his torch around him. There was only the dust and rubble of years of disuse. Nothing stirred.

After much effort, Jack succeeded in prising open the door with his screwdriver. He shone the torch around the room before entering. No footmarks disturbed the dust, cobwebs hung like festoons and a strange musty smell pervaded the atmosphere. Suddenly he became aware of an eerie feeling, as though he was being watched. Nervously, he stepped into the room and walked around, crunching the broken plaster that had fallen from the crumbling ceiling. There was no one in the room and no oil lamp, but a strange smell pervaded the air. He left the room and was about to close the door behind him when he was hit in the back by the door itself slamming shut. He turned and tried to open the door again, but it was impossible to do so. Feeling frightened by his experience, he was relieved to return to his family in the booking office.

Half an hour later the Cartwright family were in their sleeping-bags, each of them uneasy and bewildered by the recent strange events. The old building creaked occasionally, but apart from that and the rumble of distant thunder, there was silence.

At about 2am, however, Jack woke with a start. He could distinctly hear voices that seemed to be coming from the parcels office next door. Quickly putting on some clothes, he decided to investigate.

He tried the door to the parcels office, but it seemed to be locked tightly. The voices coming from the room were now audible. Jack was determined to solve the mystery. Putting his shoulder to the door, he found to his amazement that it opened easily. Looking inside, he was aware of a misty atmosphere and a figure sitting in a chair at a desk. The voices had stopped now but an illuminating mist seemed to fill the room with a white incandescent glow. The shape of the figure at the desk was vague, but distinctly human. He seemed to be poring over some papers and the room itself appeared to be tidier than when he had visited it earlier. It was as if Jack had stepped back in time to a scene from an earlier age.

Suddenly the figure seemed to become aware of Jack's presence and turned towards him, as if to ask what he wanted. Jack could see the face now, that of an elderly man with a deeply wrinkled face and steel-framed glasses. His face was gentle and benign. As Jack took a step towards the figure the mist suddenly cleared and the figure disappeared. Abruptly, Jack found himself in darkness. He switched on his torch and found himself alone in the office. He was about to shut the door when again an inexplicable force on the other side pushed it firmly shut. Jack tried the handle, but the door was locked. Totally mystified by his experience, he crept back to the booking hall and tried to sleep.

In the morning Jack related his experience to his wife, who listened sympathetically but reassured him that it must have been a nightmare. As they prepared to leave and resume their homeward journey, Jack decided to take a last look around the parcels office. Gingerly opening the door, which gave way easily, he saw the festoons of cobwebs, litter and crumbling plaster, exactly as before. Satisfied, he gently pulled the door to, which closed easily behind him. With a final look back at the station buildings, Jack drove away from the scene of his mysterious experience.

The family's first stop at a garage for repairs to the car led Jack into conversation with the proprietor. He told him about their ruined holiday and where they had spent the previous night, although he did not reveal his unusual experience.

The other man listened, then said, 'You're a braver man than I am, mister. That station is supposed to be haunted by old Garrity who was the porter there in the old days, and not many people go near it in daylight, never mind after dark.'

Jack laughed. 'Well, he didn't bother me. Perhaps we were lucky.'

30
London's most haunted underground station

The frequent manifestation of a melancholy figure at Covent Garden underground station has earned it the unwanted title of the most haunted station on the London Transport system.

The sequence of events began in the early 1960s when Jack Hayden was the station foreman. It was Christmas week (whether this time of the year had any significance or not is open to question) and Mr Hayden was in the staff mess room writing up the log book. The time was approximately 12.30am and all was quiet when suddenly the door handle rattled. Mr Hayden looked up from his writing and saw a figure dressed in old-fashioned clothes reminiscent of the style worn at the turn of the century, and whose expression was one of sadness.

Mr Hayden, who at this stage was not thinking of the supernatural, said, 'I think you are lost, sir. The lifts to the trains are upstairs.'

The stranger made no move. However, when Mr Hayden stood up and made to show the stranger the way, the figure melted into thin air, leaving the foreman completely mystified. Thinking that fatigue had got the better of his tired mind, he did not worry unduly until the following Monday morning when a porter who had been working on the station platform came to the mess room and saw a strange figure looking at Mr Hayden. As the porter entered the room the stranger melted into thin air.

The porter was so terrified that he fainted. On recovery, Mr Hayden described the stranger to the porter who agreed that it was the same figure he had seen. This traumatic experience had such a shattering effect on the porter that he left London Transport for good, swearing never to visit Covent Garden station again.

Mr Hayden, after further thoughts about the matter, decided to tell the station master, Mr Jones, about the occurrence, seeking his advice as to the right measures to adopt in these strange circumstances. Mr Jones suggested that *Psychic News* magazine should be approached with a view to investigating the incidents and perhaps providing a satisfactory answer.

Psychic News were very interested and one of their researchers visited Jack Hayden and discussed the matter in detail. It was decided that a seance should be held in the mess room and, depending on the result, they would discuss what further measures could be used to identify the ghost. The seance was held and Mr Hayden was later shown some photographs and asked if he could recognise any of the people. After examining the photographs, he recognised William Terris, who had been murdered in about 1900 in The Strand, which lies not far from Covent Garden underground station.

It is thought that William Terris was wearing evening dress, which suggests that he had visited Covent Garden Opera House nearby. However, why his ghost should have been attracted to the station and the area around the mess room has never been explained satisfactorily.

The ghost seemed to have an affinity with Mr Hayden, who saw him nearly every day in some part of the station for some two years. He did not feel afraid of the ghost and tried to speak to him, but the figure was sad and morose as if struck by a remorseless tragedy. *Psychic News* told Mr Hayden to talk to the ghost as if to help him, but no response was ever forthcoming.

Eventually, Jack Hayden was promoted to station inspector, necessitating a move away from Covent Garden station, and he was somewhat frustrated at not being able to re-establish contact with 'Charlie', as he had christened the ghost. However, it appears that many other people were destined to see William Terris, fortunately without any ill effects.

Workmen from the Maintenance Department, responsible for the smooth running of the lifts and escalators in the station, have seen William Terris's ghost on numerous occasions as they work mostly at night so that their work causes the least interference to the travelling public. Terris does not seem to mind the electricians, who undoubtedly disturb him on his preserve. One gentleman, who has not actually seen the apparition, has on several occasions heard footsteps walking up a stairway in the station. In fact, the uncertain times of Terris's appearances have had such an effect on workmen that the Maintenance Department do not allow their staff to work in the station through the night in case the ghost interferes with their potentially dangerous work. One lady who only saw Terris once would not work in the station again and demanded a move to a 'normal station'.

Jack Hayden obviously has a very close affinity with William Terris's ghost because when he made a purposeful visit to Covent Garden station recently he saw him 'as large as life', as if waiting to welcome him back.

It would therefore seem that the ghost of William Terris will haunt Covent Garden station whenever he pleases, but the cause of his frequent appearances will remain a mystery.

31
The return of the diligent signalman

*A*s we have already seen, signal boxes can be very emotive places by virtue of their often remote locations, and inexplicable events have been known to take place in them. Although today many of these vital elements of the railway system are being replaced by the larger, more modern, fully automated control centres, there still remains the lonely, isolated signal box, often miles from anywhere, which on a dark winter's night can conjure up strange happenings and instil fear even in the heart of the most level-headed signalman.

The signal box at Claxby, 2 miles from Market Rasen in Lincolnshire, was a small box constructed by the old Great Central Railway. It lay half a mile from the main road to Market Rasen and Lincoln, and about 2 miles from the attractive village of Claxby, which clings to the ironstone ridge of the Lincolnshire Wolds. This signal box was the setting for an unexplained sequence of events that to this day have puzzled the local authorities. For years, the lonely box had played its part on the busy line without anything untoward disturbing its peaceful operation. However, one night in the early 1960s its tranquillity was upset by strange occurrences.

Aubrey Clark, who for many years had worked his shifts in Claxby box, was on the night turn. Shortly after 5am the next box along the line, Holton le Moor, contacted Claxby but received no reply. Attempts were made at frequent intervals to contact Mr Clark, but without success. The signalman at Holton le Moor box became concerned and stopped the next train entering his section, asking the driver to stop at Claxby and see if everything was in order.

The driver found the box silent and Mr Clark slumped in his armchair, obviously dead. The Control Office was informed of the news and the relief signalman, Ted Hudson, who lived in Market Rasen, was summoned to take over the operation of the box. Ted knew the box intimately and had known Aubrey Clark well. When he arrived at the box, the signalman's corpse had been laid out on the signal frame and was covered with a sheet, from where it was removed by ambulance to the local hospital. The signals were at danger and the train crew were talking on the level crossing. Ted resumed the operation of the cabin and tried to shake off the depressing atmosphere that now pervaded the small room.

Mr J. Daubney, who was a relief signalman at Wrawby & Barnetby, relieved Ted at about 5.30pm. As Daubney felt that the box reeked of death, Ted decided to burn Aubrey's old armchair and replace it with another to remove the visible signs of the tragedy.

Mr Daubney was in charge of the box for the rest of that week but felt uneasy. He rang Holton le Moor frequently to talk to someone, fearing that the lonely hours would revive the still recent memories of the death of Aubrey Clark.

The following week Ted Hudson undertook the 6pm to 6am shift. The first two nights passed uneventfully, but on the third night Ted heard the sound of heavy breathing, which seemed to come from the armchair. When he rose and looked around, the breathing stopped. He walked to the door and looked out, but no one was there and all was still. But when he returned to the chair and sat down, the breathing started again. Ted convinced himself that the sounds came from the birds nesting in the eaves or the rafters and banged the walls with a brush. The wooden walls shook and the alien noise echoed around the small building, and for a time the noise stopped.

After a while, however, the heavy stentorian breathing began again. The sound was louder now and seemed to fill the box. Impatiently, Ted went outside with a brush and prodded the eaves to drive out any birds that might be disturbing his peace, but not a single one flew out. On returning to the box and resuming his duties, he was more puzzled than frightened, for he did not believe in ghosts.

The following night the same sound disturbed his normally peaceful night shift, and as he could find no logical explanation he decided to accept whatever it was, but resolved to keep the mystery to himself to avoid unkind jibes from his workmates.

On his last night shift of the week, Ted had been told that the platelaying gang would be undertaking essential track repairs near the box, starting at midnight. Unknown to Ted, however, this work was later postponed.

It was a moonlit night and from 11pm Ted was waiting for the platelayers' arrival, as their company would liven his long shift. As midnight approached he was disturbed by a terrific kick on the door. Thinking that it was the platelayers playing a joke on him, he said 'Come in', but no one entered. He had hardly sat down again when there was another strong kick at the door. 'Come in,' he repeated, but again no one entered.

Somewhat perturbed, Ted flung the door open, still believing that the platelayers were playing tricks on him. He looked outside and there at the bottom of the steps was Aubrey Clark, dressed in his motorcycle gear, his helmet glinting in the moonlight. Ted recalled that Aubrey used to travelled to work on a motor scooter, and on reaching the box he would take off his helmet and put it over one arm, while his tuck-box was held under the other. He would then climb the steps and on reaching the top would kick the door and whoever was on duty would open it for him. Ted stood and stared at the apparition in amazement, unable to believe the sight of his old friend before his eyes. Then the vision faded, leaving Ted feeling totally bemused.

A few weeks later, Ted relieved Bob Webster at about 5.45am. Bob, normally a level-headed signalman, looked ill at ease and asked Ted if he had heard any strange noises in the box. The two men exchanged experiences and found that they had heard the same noises of heavy breathing and the kick on the door. Both agreed that there would seem to be no rational explanation, and everything pointed to the fact that Aubrey Clark was revisiting his old signal box. Other signalmen had similar stories to tell and some refused to work the box, so frightened were they of the strange events. One snowy morning footprints and tyre marks were imprinted in the snow, even though Ted had received no visitor at the box.

By day Claxby signal box was warm and friendly, and it was difficult to believe that any mysterious events could have taken place there. But Ted Hudson and other signalmen like him knew that in the early hours of a winter's morning a visitation from Aubrey Clark's ghost was a real and frightening possibility.

32
The headless lover

*T*he gruesome story of the headless lover began early in the 1900s at Brooke End signal box, which controlled up and down main lines, an up goods loop and sidings used by the pick-up trains of the period.

Not far from the railway line lived a closely knit family, Mr and Mrs Gorman and their only daughter, Marion. Gorman worked on the railway as a platelayer, and occupied a small cottage maybe 200 yards from the main line. It was small and solidly constructed of red brick beneath a pantile roof in the Midland Railway's style of architecture, but adequate for the Gormans' needs and comforts. A large meadow lay in front of it and from the sash windows views of the countryside could be enjoyed. Marion loved her home, and its cosy atmosphere gave the shy girl great assurance. She was a beautiful girl with fine bones and blue eyes, her long flaxen hair giving her an almost Nordic appearance, and her clear unspoilt complexion reflecting her life in the fresh country air.

Marion had been born in this cottage and had long become used to the passage of trains and shunting movements in the adjacent sidings. She had few friends in the locality, preferring to go for long walks in the nearby countryside with the family dog, until, that is, Ronald Travis took up his duties in the signal box. He was in his late 20s, stockily built and self-sufficient, also with fair hair and blue eyes. He had proved an enthusiastic pupil when learning the complicated job of a signalman, and did not mind the night shifts or the occasional tedium of the long lonely hours. His practical disposition and dependability were appreciated by his colleagues, who welcomed his cheerfulness.

Ronald was a country lad, interested in country ways and traditions. Marion met him one night when he called to see her father on a matter appertaining to the permanent way adjacent to the signal box. For Marion and Ronald it was love at first sight. They subsequently spent all their spare time together and the courtship developed rapidly. Marion adored him and they enjoyed many happy, carefree walks together. Mr and Mrs Gorman were at first relieved that their only child had found such a solid, trustworthy young man, and encouraged the relationship, until Marion began to disappear for hours, returning home without saying where she had been. Ronald would also give no explanation when asked about her whereabouts and seemed to resent her parents' questions.

One night Mr Gorman remembered that he had to visit the box to give Travis a message about the next week's duty roster. Sighing at the thought of having to leave the warmth and comfort of the fire, he rose and lifted his coat from the hook on the kitchen door, bracing himself against the cold stormy night, then strode off into the darkness. Arriving at the signal box he mounted the steps, the handrail creaking as he used it for support. All was quiet.

The silence was explained when he entered the box and found Marion and Ronald in a deep embrace, their feelings for each other very apparent. It was now obvious where Marion had been spending so much of her time. Mr Gorman felt angry. The girl was betraying the trust that her parents had instilled into her all her young life. He realised that her reticence had been to protect the secret of her love affair with Ronald Travis. Mr Gorman lost his temper and accused Travis of luring away his daughter. In spite of the couple's protestations, he forbade Marion to meet Travis again and firmly escorted his tearful daughter home.

From then on Marion became morose and irritable. Life became difficult in the erstwhile happy home and the unfortunate girl was only allowed to go for walks in the company of her parents. One night, after a violent row, Marion ran up to her room and locked the door. Her distressed parents decided to allow her to calm down and not to disturb her, leaving her sobbing in bed. She could not sleep, however, and remembering that Ronald Travis would be on duty, decided to wait until her parents had gone to bed, then slip outside and go to the signal box to see her lover.

It was a dark night and she lay quietly until she was satisfied that her parents were asleep. Then, dressing in her long white dress, she stole quietly downstairs and made her way down the path to the gate and across the meadow to the railway line. The all-enveloping darkness made her progress difficult, but in her emotional state she staggered on. Reaching the railway fence she climbed over and started across the tracks. In the distance she could hear a train coming and could see the yellow lights of the oil lamps in the signal box. The oncoming train drew nearer. She was gasping, but she knew that she could beat it if she ran. She had not much further to go and soon she would be safe in her lover's arms.

Safely over the down line, she started to cross the up line, but stumbled and fell. With the train rapidly bearing down on her she stood no chance. The vigilant driver, seeing her white-clad body almost in front of his engine, applied his brakes and slammed shut the regulator. He and his fireman felt the terrifying impact as the engine passed over her, the wheels severing her head from her body. By this time Travis was on the horrible scene of the accident, the bloodstained white dress revealing a gruesome sight. He raced to the Gormans' cottage and with great difficulty told the distressed couple what had happened.

The ensuing enquiries and inquest returned a verdict of accidental death and the sad interlude closed, apparently the end of a tragic love affair. Travis was transferred to another area and the life of the signal box returned to normal.

Then in the late 1940s a series of incidents happened that were to cause distress and horror. At dawn one spring morning a heavily loaded freight train, headed by a pre-war 2-8-0 locomotive, was running out of steam owing to a badly clinkered fire-bed as it approached Brooke End signal box. The signalman, knowing that this train had been in his section for some time and was overdue, set his points and signal from the up main to the up goods loop to allow a following passenger train to run past without any unnecessary delay. As the freight train came slowly to a halt at the loop stop signal near the box, the fireman told the signalman of their problem, who in turn reported the incident to the Control. The engine driver also gave Control some idea of how long it would take to clean the fire and raise sufficient steam for him to take his train forward.

Meanwhile, the train guard, George Marsh, decided to make himself a mug of tea. Standing on the brake-van verandah, he looked down the line towards the signal box. Suddenly he saw a white figure slowly crossing the main line towards Brooke End signal box. She was obviously taking a risk as the up passenger train was almost due and the up main signals had been cleared. In fact, the approaching train was already audible.

He jumped down quickly from his brake-van and ran down the line shouting a warning. The figure, that of a young girl dressed in a white dress, appeared to stumble and fall and then, as he drew nearer, she rose to her feet and staggered towards the signal box steps. He stopped dead in his tracks, rooted to the spot with horror. The white-clad figure had no head and there were blood-stains on the front of her dress. The horrific apparition disappeared as it reached the foot of the steps.

On hearing George Marsh shout, then scream, those in the box looked out and saw momentarily the terrifying apparition seconds before it disappeared. The goods train driver was the first to recover his scattered wits and went down the steps to comfort Marsh who was leaning against the tender side, shaking uncontrollably, his face ashen. He assisted Marsh up the steps to the box and, seating him in the signalman's battered but comfortable old armchair, reported the incident to Control, requesting medical assistance for the unfortunate guard, who was obviously unable to continue his duties.

Others who have had the misfortune to witness the headless apparition wish to remain anonymous. Their memories are so vivid and horrific that they wish to forget them.

Railway modernisation meant that eventually Brooke End signal box was abandoned, its structure left to stand forlorn. The windows were broken and the inside of the box completely vandalised. Dark, scorched areas suggested that an unsuccessful attempt had been made to set fire to it. The box seemed resigned to its fate of demolition. When that day came, perhaps the tragic story of a love-sick young girl trying to find solace in the arms of her lover would be laid to rest for ever.

33
Fear on the fish dock

*T*his totally unexplained mystery took place in the 1950s in a siding that ran parallel to Fish Dock Road, a main arterial road giving access to Grimsby Fish Docks. The railway line ran between various buildings and a high wooden fence that was used for part of its length for advertisement hoardings. Railwaymen who worked in the area had been so overcome by a feeling of evil that pervaded a particular location that many refused to work the night shift, which involved going near the place in question.

It was the custom of the train crews to make up the fish trains from empty stock located in the New Clee sidings, between Grimsby and Cleethorpes. From there the vans would be collected by the ex-Great Central Railway Fish Dock tankers (small outside-cylinder 0-6-0 side-tank locomotives of a short-wheelbase design for working the tight curves on the docks) and pushed up the fish jetty for loading with fish for dispatch to such places as Leicester and Banbury as part of the express fish train service offered by the railway.

One Monday night around midnight, some 35 vans had been brought up from New Clee sidings, pushed down Melhuish's jetty, loaded up, and brought back to the middle road alongside Fish Dock Road. The shunters who rode on the engine then alighted and went down the train to connect up the vacuum brake pipes, or 'bags'.

The night was dark and still, the middle road had an eerie, forbidding atmosphere, and the street lights threw strange shadows among the hoardings. The shunters shuddered as they went about their work. That particular night seemed strangely different, and the dark shadows seemed even more menacing than usual.

When the 'bags' had been connected and the brake was continuous through the train, the engine driver 'blew up' the vacuum to get the required pressure of 21 inches. On this occasion he could only get 5 inches, so he told one of the shunters, George Dyson, what had happened and asked him to go back along the fish vans and find out if a 'bag' was off, allowing air into the system. Armed with a lamp, Dyson set off to check the connections.

'Have you found anything?' asked the driver on his return.

Dyson shook his head. 'Everything's all right. Try your pressure now.' But the dial still only showed 5 inches.

'There's still something wrong,' said the driver.

Jack St Pierre, another shunter on the same gang, was asked to go and check the pipes. In spite of his powerful torch, as he slowly made his way along the train of fish vans the darkness seemed to close in on him and he felt a weird, evil presence as if something might spring out from between the silent wagons and overpower him. As he shone his torch on the connections the light seemed to dim, which was not reassuring. About three-quarters of the way down the train Jack began to feel very frightened as the overpowering sense of impending evil became even stronger. Yet he still could not find the offending connection. He felt his nerve breaking and terror began to overtake his mind. A horrible damp stifling smell then filled his lungs. He could go no further, so turned and ran terrified back to the engine.

Fighting for breath, he called up to the driver, 'I can't find anything amiss,' then walked towards his workmates who were standing talking.

Once more the driver tried the vacuum and again could only get 5 inches. By this time he was obviously annoyed.

'Come here, you lot,' he said. 'Now, what's going on? There must be a bag off somewhere. How is it you can't find it?'

The men stared silently at each other, then one plucked up courage and said, 'There's something not quite right down there', pointing to the line of fish vans.

The driver, now glowing with impatience, agreed volubly.

'You're absolutely right!' he snarled. 'I can't get any vacuum pressure. What's the matter with you? Have you seen a ghost or something?'

Dyson replied, 'No, we haven't seen a ghost. But I can't explain it, it's as if the devil himself is down there, and there's this horrible smell that chokes you and at the same time you get the feeling that something evil is lying in wait for you. And another thing, the torch goes dim as if it's losing its power. It's so frightening, I'm scared and I'm not going back there – I just don't know what's going on.'

His mates nodded and one said, 'I agree with George – I've never known such a feeling of evil and I'm not risking my neck for anyone.'

He switched on his torch and the powerful beam clove the darkness like a white spear. 'See that?' he said. 'Nothing's wrong with the torch now, but down there it nearly went out.'

The driver, now totally exasperated, climbed down from the engine. 'Now look, I'll come with you. Pass me the torch, Mick. Now we'll see what's going on.'

The men set off in fear and trepidation, singing and whistling to bolster their courage. The driver led the way, turning round periodically to check that the others were with him. Then, nearing the end of the line of vans, to his surprise he became aware of a feeling of dread pervading the atmosphere. He turned to find the shunters huddled together.

'Come on, let's look for this bag,' he said.

Unenthusiastically the men shone their torches around the couplings and flexible connections, but each and every one of them was aware of the overpowering feeling of evil. Eventually the offending bag was found and re-connected by trembling hands. Their duty done, the whole gang ran as fast as possible back to the engine and gathered in the cab. After they had regained their breath and composure, they all swore that they would never again frequent that evil place. Subsequent investigation failed to produce any reason why such an atmosphere should pervade the location.

Some years later a tragic event happened on the line. A well-known member of a prominent fishing company whose life had been plagued by tragedy and illness decided to commit suicide.

On the particular afternoon that he decided to end his life he had been watching the marshalling of the fish vans from his office window. He waited for the right moment, walked calmly across the road, knelt down, put his neck across the railway line and waited for a loaded van to sever it. The forces of evil must have been working smoothly that day because it so happened that the spot he chose was within yards of the epicentre of terror that had frightened the railwaymen so many years earlier. One is left to wonder if the malevolent unseen spirit was waiting to claim its victim, having been unable to satisfy its evil appetite.

Nothing untoward has happened at that spot since, and today the track has gone and a road covers the scene, affording no clue as to the evil influence that lurked under the hoardings of Fish Dock Road.

34
'Arnold' and the green Morris Minor

*I*n the first premonition, Mr Reynolds saw himself standing on the footplate of No 43106 leaving Bridgnorth, smokebox leading, with some covered wagons heading for Bewdley. As the locomotive cab began to cross the bridge, the first full-span cross-beam collapsed as a green Morris Minor car was passing underneath. The cab was filled with steam and flame as the engine fell through the bridge. At this point the premonition ended.

Mr Reynolds's second premonition again took place on the footplate of No 43106 leaving Bridgnorth. He saw himself look back along the train, then remember the first premonition. Realising the impending danger, he looked up the road, where he saw a Morris Minor coming down the hill. He told the driver to stop as the bridge was going to collapse. When the driver refused, Mr Reynolds climbed off the engine and watched it fall through the bridge on to the car, steam and smoke erupting from the cab as it did so. The first wagon fell on to the wreckage and so the premonition ended.

The third and final premonition took place on the corner of the castle walk. Mr Reynolds saw an engine leaving Bridgnorth and a green Morris Minor coming down the hill towards the bridge. As the cab of the engine moved on to the bridge the engine fell through, the cab falling first, on to the car that was passing underneath.

Mr Reynolds related these premonitions solely to his wife Ruth. A few weeks later Ruth was told by a Mr Walker of a premonition that he had had the previous night – it was identical to that of Mr Reynolds. Mr Reynolds therefore decided that it was time to visit the bridge and examine the area. He discovered loose rivets and serious fretting that had occurred between the main beam and the first three cross-beams on the right-hand side only.

The bridge had been cleaned and repainted two years earlier and had been found to be sound. At the time Mr Reynolds himself had looked out of curiosity and everything had seemed to be in order. On discovering the fretting, he informed the Chief Civil Engineer who imposed a strict speed limit on the bridge. A new bridge was fitted some three months later during the winter.

Meanwhile, about six months after Mr Reynolds's first premonition he experienced unexplained noises, mainly thumping and banging. One night he and his wife witnessed a vague aura of human form on the firebox top of No 43106. It lasted about a minute before fading, and they both sensed a feeling of impending danger. After the bridge was repaired, 'Arnold', as they named the apparition, disappeared. Mr Reynolds believes that he was a ghost of the future, possibly of someone who was not supposed to die should the bridge collapse – in other words, the driver of No 43106, the driver of the green Morris Minor or Mr Reynolds himself.

On another occasion Mr Reynolds had just gone to bed when he had the feeling that there was a fire on the site. He dressed himself, borrowed a torch and went outside. He walked along Platform 2 and noticed smoke coming from the signal box. By the time he reached the box the first flames had started. Although the fire was put out in 20 minutes, about £3,000 worth of damage was done, mainly to the electrical system and interlocking mechanism.

Whether 'Arnold' could be blamed for the fire, Mr Reynolds could not be sure, but his comings and goings certainly seemed to leave a trail of mystery and unease. For him, Bridgnorth would always be associated with the antics of a ghost that obviously liked railway engines and would appear from time to time to warn of impending accidents.

35
The mysterious passenger

One morning a gentleman left Euston station, London, with some important papers that he intended to read on his journey. The guard found him an empty compartment and locked the door. As the train was departing, an elderly man hurriedly boarded and entered the compartment where the solitary occupant was studying his documents. The two men eventually fell into conversation, the late-comer explaining that he was a director of the railway company and that he was interested in a new branch line that was to be opened. He was also carrying £70,000, which he was depositing in a bank for payment for the work that had just been completed.

The late-comer said to his travelling companion, 'By the way, I know the house that you are visiting. The lady is my niece. Tell her that I hope the next time I come to stay she won't have such a huge fire in the Blue Room.'

As the train was approaching the director's station, he rose to his feet and drew from his pocket a visiting card bearing the name Dwerringhouse, which he gave to his companion. After he had left the train, the remaining passenger noticed a cigar-case lying on the floor. He picked it up and ran out on to the platform, hoping to return it to its owner. He managed to catch a brief glimpse of him talking to a man at the end of the platform; the man's hair was sandy in colour and his face was distinctly visible. However, unaccountably the two men disappeared, and a porter was unable to help as he had not seen either of them. The gentleman returned to his compartment and resumed his journey, puzzled by his strange experience.

Having reached his destination, he remembered the message that he had been asked to give to his hostess.

'I travelled down with an uncle of yours and he told me to give you the following message,' he said. Both the lady and her husband were obviously distressed at the message regarding the huge fire in the Blue Room. That evening, when the ladies retired, the husband explained that the message had been very embarrassing to his wife since her uncle had disappeared with £70,000 and the police were looking for him. It so happened that directors of the railway company who were also house guests overheard this conversation, and subsequently asked the gentleman if he would appear before the board and tell the story of his journey and travelling companion.

In due course the meeting took place. As he was relating his story, the gentleman suddenly realised that sitting before him among the directors was the sandy-haired man he had seen talking to Mr Dwerringhouse. He was a cashier with the company, and immediately protested his innocence; he said that he had been away on holiday at the time. However, the directors insisted that the cashier's records be examined and it soon became clear that there were discrepancies in the accounts. The cashier eventually broke down and confessed that he had accidentally killed Mr Dwerringhouse knowing that he would be carrying £70,000. He intended to use the cash to repay the money he had stolen from the company. He had waylaid Mr Dwerringhouse and hit him on the head to stun him, but in falling to the ground the older man had hit his head on a large stone, sustaining a fatal blow.

The curious episode of the cigar-case was also explained. Owing to some essential repairs, the carriage in which Mr Dwerringhouse had travelled had been out of use from the day of his journey to his subsequent ghostly appearance. The guard at Euston was positive that on that particular day he had locked the door of the compartment and that there was only one gentleman inside when the train left the station.

36
The phantom goods train

*I*n order to explain fully the story of the Louth-Bardney goods train it will be helpful to describe the line's history and situation. Louth, 16 miles south of Grimsby, is a pleasant Lincolnshire market town. Born with the formation of the East Lincolnshire Railway Company in 1848, by the 1870s, as part of the Great Northern Railway, the station had become an important junction, the hub of the local railway system, with its main line from Grimsby to Boston, Spalding and Peterborough running north and south, a branch going south-east to Mablethorpe and Sutton-on-Sea, and one going west through the Lincolnshire Wolds towards Bardney and Lincoln.

The latter was planned to be an important branch, conveying iron ore from the strata at Apley and Donington, but this traffic never materialised owing to the vast amount of iron ore deposits found at Santon, near Scunthorpe. However, it became a boon to the local farming community, being used extensively to convey agricultural products and large amounts of sugar beet to the large processing factory at Bardney. With its sylvan setting, meandering through the scenic beauty of the Wolds, it was often called the 'Bluebell line'.

When the line first opened the service consisted of eight passenger trains a day, four in each direction, and two daily goods trains, six days a week. As was common with branch lines, engines of an older and secondary nature would be used; thus Sturrock 0-6-0 tender engines were known to operate on the goods and sometimes the passenger trains. Later engines of Stirling and Ivatt vintage found their way down the single-line branch.

Passenger traffic was never profitable, but as a link between the two towns it was used by the sparse population as and when required. During the First World War the traffic increased with the requirements of the armed forces, as was also the case in the Second World War; a great deal of traffic was involved in moving ammunition and bombs for the many airfields in the vicinity. After 1945 the motor car made a significant impact on the travelling public, and lorries and buses took a considerable amount of business from the railway, so it was inevitable that management, casting a critical eye over expenditure on branch lines, however scenic, considered most of these rural lines as financially unviable. In 1951, therefore, the last passenger train ran on the Louth-Bardney line. Freight services ran until 1956, then all services ceased and the track was lifted as far as Bardney, although the Bardney-Lincoln portion remained.

Although this seemed to be the end of the Louth-Bardney line, it refused to die. It seems as though some supernatural force was intent on operating the branch. At Hallington (the first station from Louth) people heard sounds of a distant train approaching the village. It was rumoured that, even though the track had been lifted for some years, the 'train' actually came into Hallington station and blew off steam.

Having heard the stories, the author decided to investigate them for himself together with a friend. One night in August 1969, therefore, the two men drove to Hallington to reconnoitre the line. They found that the trackbed was still in good condition and that the well-preserved station house was inhabited by a local shepherd, who was not prepared to make any comment on the subject of the ghost train.

The two friends took stock of everything in the immediate vicinity. On their left was a field of sheep, while to their right was a grass field that appeared to be uninhabited. It was a perfect summer's night, warm and still. At 11.45pm the two men listened and waited in silence. Then they heard the unexpected faint sound of a train, seemingly working hard. The sound became louder until the occasional snatch of wagon couplings and the unmistakable clank of side rods could be heard. So intrigued and frightened were the two men by this unusual experience that they listened without uttering a word. The sound seemed to come in waves, getting louder and louder, then fading away. For what seemed an age, they felt gripped with terror and unable to move, mesmerised by the ethereal sound. Then, as if to break the spell, the sheep dogs began to bark frenziedly and the nearby sheep stampeded as if they sensed impending danger.

The sheep eventually settled down, and the dogs' barking receded into a whimpering. The men strained their ears for continuing sounds of the ghostly train. It had receded on a faint wave of sound, but it was possible to imagine it working hard against the up-grade of the Withcall Tunnel cutting. Gradually even the faintest sound died away. The sheep became placid once again and the dogs were quiet, probably asleep.

The two friends discussed their experience on the way home. They checked their notes. They had not been dreaming. They had without doubt heard a train. What had startled the dogs, whose frenzied barking had disturbed the sheep? The visitation of the phantom train had made the dogs aware of an unusual happening. Why had the train run again? Was it the call of a soul in torment? Why had the two men been favoured with a sound of the supernatural? There can be little doubt that it was the supernatural echo of a train that had once run along that peaceful little branch line.

Others who visited the line subsequently to share the experience were not favoured with the sound of the ghostly train. A local farmer had installed a grain-drier in the immediate locality, which may have prevented any such manifestation from being heard. However, reliable reports have been received since 1969 that the ghostly train still runs along the old Louth-Bardney line, all accounts bearing witness to this remarkable phenomenon.

37
The ghosts of Rothley station

Stuart Bailey, station master of Rothley on the preserved Great Central Railway, has heard many stories of ghosts that have appeared at his station, although he himself has no first-hand experiences of the supernatural.

One tale was told to him as recently as August 1983. The story began when a young man attended a party in Mournacre Hill, a suburb of Leicester. It was very late when he left the party, and as he was unable to obtain transport to his home in Mountsorrel, he decided to walk along the old trackbed from Belgrave to Rothley station, this being the most direct route home. In view of what occurred later, one may believe that the young man was intoxicated. However, undoubtedly the night air would have had a sobering effect, especially as the walk was some 3 miles.

Being the dead of night, the man was uncertain of how to leave the railway and at Rothley he walked up on to the platform. There by the light of an adjacent street lamp he clearly saw the figure of a station master or porter wearing a flat-topped regulation hat apparently waiting for a train. This was at about 2am on a Sunday morning and the sight of the apparition frightened him. The young man ran across the goods yard and eventually found the gate on to the road. On relating the story to Mr Bailey, the man asked whether a train service was running at that time of night. The answer was negative.

Another well-known and frequently reported story is that of a man and his dog at Swithland. Bridge No 352 carries the line across the country road from Rothley plain to Swithland village at Swithland Sidings. To the south, bridge No 354 is that at Rothley Station, half a mile away. Traces of the structure of the missing intermediate bridge can be seen at the far end of Swithland cutting north of the station. It was a farm occupation bridge under the railway connecting Swithland Lane to the east of the line with fields to the west. The bridge was filled in many years ago when houses spread along this part of Swithland Lane.

Before the Second World War a local man had some pens in the field on the western side of the line in which he reared pigs and poultry. In midwinter the track beneath this bridge became a muddy morass, so at night, when he could not be seen by the signalman in Swithland box, he and his dog, who were inseparable, used to cross over the railway lines. One night in the early years of the war both he and his dog were killed by a passing train. From then on until the line was closed by BR both man and dog were seen on many occasions from Swithland signal box and the platform at Rothley station.

Strange figures have also appeared on the arcaded station entrance stairs at Rothley, so the area seems to be favoured by visitations of ghostly phenomena.

38
The platelayers' hut

During my researches for material to complete this book I have found that railwaymen in particular have been reluctant to allow their names to be used in a story, and have sometimes insisted that even the name of the location be changed; perhaps they fear leg-pulling from their workmates!

The following tale was recalled by a retired platelayers' ganger who, as expected, has asked me to change his name for the purpose of this story. He also requested that the name of the location be altered. 'It's between Louth and Willoughby but I'm not saying exactly or we'll have the whole world knowing!' And he would not be drawn any further, so now read on.

I was told of the story by a friend who knew the old platelayer, whom we shall call Fred. My friend Harry (a retired driver) fixed up a meeting at a local pub and we were able to talk and discuss the strange happenings. Fred's story concerned a lineside hut used by the permanent way men, also known as platelayers or lengthmen, which was situated in a cutting on the trackbed of the old East Lincolnshire line that before its closure had run between Grimsby and Peterborough via Boston; we are talking about the southern section of this once busy line.

What was so special about this old sleeper-built hut, one side of which had been used by the men to keep their tools and equipment in, and the other to take shelter from the elements?

The local children used to play in the cutting and had for a long time fancied the hut as a den or HQ for their games, but one end of it was always locked by a large padlock securing a hasp that was red with rust but which still secured the door. Some of the more irresponsible youths had tried to set fire to the building, but somehow it did not catch, much to their disappointment! The windows had been broken years ago but the railway company had boarded up the frames with wooden battens, which were very effective; they did, however, allow a view into the building.

All was uneventful until one child came home and told his mother that he had met a 'funny old man' in the cutting, 'dressed in funny old clothes'. The child was emphatic, 'but he just went away – we looked for him but couldn't find him.'

His mother reassured him that 'people often go down there with their dogs; don't worry, I'm sure he wouldn't hurt you, but perhaps you shouldn't go down there for a week or two, David.'

A few weeks later, and quite unrelated to David's experience, a group of children from a neighbouring village made their way over the fields for a walk with their dogs. They found the cutting and scrambled down the slope, enjoying the freedom. The old hut looked interesting and they soon explored the area, which had reverted back to nature, the flora and fauna re-establishing its claim to colonise the old trackbed.

The children found that the hut door opened easily enough, and cautiously ventured in. The place smelled musty and stale but it fascinated them. The remains of a table and chair told of more ordered times, spiders were everywhere, and a mouse scuttled across the dirty floor, startling the younger children who squeaked with fear. Chattering excitedly, the children tried to open the door to the other part of the building, but it was still padlocked securely. They could see a little through various cracks but there seemed to be nothing of interest there.

One more adventurous boy decided to explore the overgrown slope behind the hut and he was pushing his way through the undergrowth when he caught sight of a figure approaching the hut further down the slope; the boy was close enough to see that the figure was that of a tramp wearing tattered clothing and crowned with a battered trilby hat. When the figure looked up the boy was impressed by bright, blue eyes and a long nose, but a kind expression. Taken by surprise and fear, the boy lost his balance and tumbled down the grassy bank towards the stranger, but before the boy's incredulous gaze the figure melted into thin air.

The other children, hearing the boy's cries, ran to him and he told them what had happened. They searched the cutting and the area around the hut without success. The other children pulled his leg and generally teased him about what he had seen, but the child strenuously defended his story; somehow the fun had gone out of the adventure and they decided to return home.

The other boy, David, was also puzzling about his experience in the cutting, and resolved to go back and try to find out if he had been dreaming; somehow he did not feel frightened but more determined to see the tramp and make friends with him. One night, when his parents were out, David returned to the scene. As expected, everything was quiet – not even a walker with a dog was passing through. David cautiously approached the old hut and peered through a crack in the battens before going round to the door, which to his surprise was ajar. Very slowly he entered the hut. There was no one there, no sign of life, only cobwebs and neglect.

As he turned he caught a glimpse of something go past the open door, and dashed outside in time to see the figure of the old tramp going towards the slope as if to climb up and away. David ran after him; he was nearly at the top, almost over the lip of the cutting, when he looked round to face the boy and smiled. Then to David's amazement he disappeared. The boy searched around the area but the man, or whatever it had been, had gone, leaving the boy bewildered and confused.

When he arrived home his parents were there and he was able to tell them what had happened; their first reaction was one of anger at his disregard of their wishes, but they were interested in his story. Afterwards David's father decided to consult the local policeman to ask his views about the affair.

When he was told about the strange experiences, the policeman said, 'I think I remember a tale long ago about a similar matter,' he said, rubbing his chin. 'Some years ago a platelayer named Jed Knighton opted out of the rat race and became what I suppose you'd call a tramp. He wandered about this neck of the woods and he was quite harmless – he was fond of children. Anyway, he lived in the old hut after the railway was taken up, and we didn't see much of him in the winter, but when the spring came round he would appear again. Then one year – I can't remember when – we missed him. Some of us worried and went looking for him, then one of Alf Wood's sons found him dead in the old pw hut. We think he died of a heart attack, or so the doctor said. Not a mark on him, so it must have been natural causes; anyway, it would seem that he comes back to his old home. I'd heard tales about some people having seen an old man down there, but not for a long while. He wouldn't hurt anyone, so your lad needn't be scared of him.'

Fred says that was the last sighting of the spirit of Jed Knighton, so his soul found its peace at last.

39
Strange experiences at
Walton Junction

*I*t was during the summer months of 1968 that my father first
began to take me to Walton Junction, Liverpool, to see what
must have been the very last of the steam trains thunder past. I
loved trains, but can remember the mounting excitement that I
felt as we approached the path leading to the station change
suddenly and inexplicably to fear.

The path ran parallel to the lines and the junction signal box
northwards towards the station itself. The fear always came when
I was about halfway down the path. There was a strange feel
about the place as though somebody or something was watching.
It always seemed to mar our visits. The eyes even seemed to
watch me when, during the autumn, I picked wild blackberries at
the end of the platform.

One particular Easter, a beautiful day, I remember an absolute
terror overwhelming me with as we stood outside the ticket
office after returning from a journey. It was indescribable, and I
have intensely disliked that spot ever since.

During the damp November evenings when the gas lamps
flickered in the wind, nothing would convince me that danger
wasn't lurking in the eerie shadows. During the summer of 1975
I visited the station with two friends one day when we had
nothing particular to do. I was astonished, as we began to walk
down the now weed-strewn path, to feel the familiar sensation of
fear and expectation. Both my friends also felt that there was
something 'queer' about the place and we left quickly.

A few weeks later we returned, this time with a third friend, a very level-headed girl. We told her nothing of our horrible experience. This time we settled in the deserted waiting room, which was silent and cold. After a very short time we all felt a horrible feeling of being watched and an intangible atmosphere of dread and doom. The girl was very scared and wanted to go at once, feeling that we were in definite danger from something. We left as darkness was descending on that foreboding place and nothing could have made us stay or convinced us that there was not nothing awful waiting in the station.

Recently I returned to Walton Junction with my children to get the train to Ormskirk. We used the same old path, and I was amazed to realise that without knowing it I had been hurrying my children along and constantly looking over my shoulder. I was convinced something was following us, though nothing was visible.

We paused on the small bridge that led to the ticket office. I looked at the now derelict railway cottages that stood silent, lost and forlorn. The feeling of fear had subsided somewhat and I remembered looking into the rubble-strewn backyards and thinking how sad it was that they were now in ruin, as the last time I was at the station they were occupied. Suddenly we all heard a loud bang from the back bedroom of the second cottage, as though a door had been slammed hard.

It was a cold, calm day with no wind. We waited to see if anyone came out, maybe a cat or a dog, but everywhere was silent and still. In any event, there was so much rubbish and broken glass littered about that it would have been difficult for anyone to climb out without making a lot of noise.

So we left and resumed our journey. The uncanny, oppressive atmosphere still hangs over that spot as it has done for more than 25 years.

40
The Ramsey mystery

*T*he Isle of Man's narrow-gauge railway has brought pleasure
and fascination to many people, either as holidaymakers or
railway enthusiasts, since the 1870s. This story involves a youth
hostel in the town of Ramsey; let Mr J. Glasscock of Braintree,
Essex, tell the story.

'I can be reasonably precise about the date and time of the
occurrence; it was at the Ramsey hostel, the time was 11.30pm
one day in late July 1967, and I think it was a Wednesday. That
was the year that the Isle of Man Railway re-opened and I was
feeling very emotional about the whole affair, with good
reason, as the idea of the Isle of Man without a railway was
quite unthinkable. I did actually get over to work for them in
1968-70 and 1971, but this story took place in 1967 when I
was just paying a visit and was given a bed for the night in the
hostel. There are two things to note about Ramsey station:
first, its extension line, the harbour branch, had closed years
before, and second, no engine was ever kept at the station
overnight because the shed water supply had been
disconnected.
    So I, and the only other lad in the dormitory who was a railway
enthusiast, were surprised and stunned to hear, just as we were
slipping off to sleep, the sound of wagons being shunted in the
station. Wagons have a different coupling system over in the
island; the sound of Isle of Man shunting is quite different from
mainland shunting – you don't get the clunk of the links as on a
loose-coupled wagon but a delayed clank as the 'chopper' of one
drops over the buffing plate of another. When you have listened

to it as many times as we had, you get to recognise the unique sound – it is absolutely unmistakable.

At first we could only hear the wagons and we thought that it could be someone hand-shunting – but at that time of night? Also we couldn't understand why, since there were only three trains a day each way, and only the 11.50am arrival and the 4.05pm departure were ever heavy trains. We only knew for certain that there was something strange afoot when we heard the sounds of a train being marshalled, and it started coming towards the hostel; what was more terrifying was that it was coming on a non-existent track! Had it been a real train the sound would have faded off towards the west – away from the hostel. Now we could hear the engine as well; it came towards the hostel over the non-existent harbour branch and clattered to a stop, perhaps at one of the wharves. We heard one final hiss of the safety valves, then silence.

There were seven people in our dormitory and I think five were awake; we all heard the mysterious sounds without any doubt, but it appeared that none of the inhabitants of the other dormitories heard anything at all. We, of course, went outside to see if we could see anything, not really expecting to, but there was nothing to suggest the passage of a train, just the cool night air and the distant sounds of night life – nothing to prove or disprove the eerie sounds that we had heard so clearly.

Had it been wishful thinking? Could I have been dreaming? I think not, as four other unsolicited accounts verified my experience. We had been privy to a re-enactment of the movements of a former working on the old harbour branch, and although not frightened we were all very puzzled by the strange sequence of events.'

41
Ashton Moss Junction

*T*here would appear to be a considerable number of strange events concerning signal boxes and their environs, more so than other areas of unexplained activities on the railway. Here is another story, again entirely without explanation; this one concerns Ashton Moss Junction, but let Mr Ian McGill reveal the mystery.

'This story concerns a location about three-quarters of a mile west of Ashton-under-Lyme station, where a freight-only line from Denton Junction on the Stockport to Stalybridge line bifurcates to join the Manchester to Huddersfield trans-Pennine route by way of west- and east-facing curves. The point of bifurcation at the southernmost point of the triangle is Ashton Moss South Junction, whilst the western and eastern points of convergence with the Manchester to Huddersfield line are known respectively as Ashton Moss North Junction and OA&GB (Oldham, Ashton & Guide Bridge) Junction.

My informant (who wishes to be anonymous but is nevertheless truthful) had spent a short time in his early days as a signalman at OA&GB Junction signal box. While on duty one Saturday afternoon during the early part of 1975, he heard the sound of footsteps ascending the steps leading up to the box, then became aware of the figure of a man about to enter the vestibule outside the door. Expecting a knock to gain admittance, the signalman walked towards the door to see what the visitor wanted. However, the anticipated knock never came and, opening the door of the box, the signalman found the vestibule silent and totally devoid of anyone; the man had vanished without trace. The signalman went down the steps to search for signs of the visitor, but there was no one about – a complete mystery.

The brief glimpse the signalman gained of the stranger was not sufficient to give a good description except that he was male and appeared to be carrying a bag. Was this the shade of a railwayman visiting his former workplace? Could he have been a signalman who met an unfortunate death and still haunted the place of his demise?

The following Saturday afternoon, my informant was once again on duty when the light began to fade – he hated the short winter days. Suddenly he heard a sound, a strange sound of movement below the box. He went to the top of the steps and looked around, but couldn't see anyone or anything untoward; but when he looked out of the window he thought he saw a figure on the track.

The signalman at Ashton Moss South Junction box, about 200 yards away to the south, also became aware of someone trespassing out on the track, in the vicinity of a road bridge that spanned the line near the junction. After conferring, the two signalmen decided to try and apprehend the person concerned, and after making sure that Control had been told of the situation and the boxes were safe to leave, they walked towards each other, approaching the trespasser from opposite directions, so keeping him in view all the time and affording him little chance of escape. Nevertheless, on reaching the spot where they had seen the person loitering, there was no one to be seen.

I don't have to stress the danger of anyone moving about on a railway track; ignorance is no excuse for trespassing on railway property and the warning notices are always abundant, which is the reason that the two men were so concerned, first for the person's safety and second for the risk of a collision with a train and the undoubted injuries that would result. The two men were not concerned with ghosts, only the safe operation of the signal boxes and their environs.

The person they sought had disappeared into thin air; it was only then that they wondered whether the dusk had deceived them. I could understand one man imagining that he saw a person in the immediate area of the box, but it is hard to believe that two level-headed signalmen could have been mistaken enough to be confused by the same phenomenon. My informant thinks that what he saw was genuine and was certain that someone was down there; his mate in the other box was equally sure that he too saw the figure. If any person had authority to be in the vicinity he would have been wearing a high visibility vest, as laid down in the regulations – it would be madness not to do so.

I am told that other people have had similar experiences but are not prepared to enlarge on their stories; perhaps they had seen a ghost of a long-gone railwayman who had worked in the area years ago and had come back to his earthly place of employment. The mystery remains and perhaps will never be solved, but one thing is certain – those two signalmen were absolutely sure of what they had seen and were unshakeable in their beliefs.'

42
Lyonshall station

*T*he village of Lyonshall in Herefordshire near the Welsh Borders was provided with a station by the Great Western Railway. This small railway outpost had a somewhat chequered history and a rather inconsistent patronage, and closure came entirely on 1 January 1917 in the midst of the First World War. However, some five years later the GWR had a change of heart and decided to re-open the station to goods traffic on 18 September 1922. Subsequent re-opening to passengers on 11 December of that year heralded a new era for the station and trade seemed to have awakened to the transport needs of the community.

But during the next wartime emergency, when one would imagine that *all* railway stations would be needed, the axe fell again on Lyonshall, and it was closed to all traffic on 1 July 1940 and abandoned.

My correspondent, Mr Glasscock, has a very strange tale to tell.

'During the hot summer of 1959, on a particularly heavy and sultry day, I and a friend visited Lyonshall station. We were on a cycling holiday, and being very interested in railways generally, I liked looking over old stations.

Lyonshall station was – and I very much doubt that any trace of it remains today – in a very dangerous condition. The bridge had been removed but the wooden platform and building were visible from the road below. There was a roofed stairway leading to platform level, with every step either missing or rotten, so the bottom of the staircase was made completely inaccessible with barbed wire criss-crossed right up to the old roof-beam. Over the years brambles had spread in all directions and had wound round the barbed wire, so it would have taken an axe or some other sharp tool to have gained entry – one certainly couldn't have reached the top of the stairway at all.

I remarked to my friend, 'You'd have to wait for a long time to get a train from here,' and he smiled as we both set off for the youth hostel down the road. I believe that is also closed now.

In the morning, although our route lay the other way, I insisted on going back to the old station for one more look. It seemed sad to see the old place decaying, uncared for and neglected. I was convinced that something had happened in our absence, and something had indeed happened.

It had rained hard during the night and early morning – which was strange for that summer when we had a period of almost drought conditions. Anyway, the steps that remained, and there weren't many of them, were still damp, since the roof of the stairway was as rotten as everything else. But clearly visible and definitely new since the previous evening was a set of footprints, small hobnailed boot tracks going up the staircase to the top and not coming down. I shuddered – the very thought of anyone being so foolish baffled me. The steps were so rotten that it wouldn't have taken any weight to have snapped them and sent anyone plunging down, causing a bad injury.

The prints were about my own size, 6½, and my own guess, for what it is worth – since, as a cadet, I did own a pair of hobnails – is that my own almost religious love of country railways had revealed a kind of secular stigmatic effect. My friend was most unimpressed – he could see the footprints but shrugged his shoulders and suggested that we move on. However, the mystery remains and I will never forget it, and will always puzzle over the mysterious footprints that defied all the obstacles – or did they?'

43
The scent of roses

Charlotte Campbell was more than delighted to have received a reply to her letter for the position of children's nanny, which she had seen advertised in *The Times*. She had hoped for a reply, but dared not hope too much; she imagined that the Hon Mrs Anderson-Hunt would have had many replies, and perhaps ladies with experience would be far more preferable to a young, comparatively inexperienced girl like herself. But in 1906 it was the accepted procedure to reply to letters and Charlotte was very excited at the invitation to visit Winstable Hall for an interview.

The Hon Mrs Anderson-Hunt had sent 10 shillings for Charlotte's train fare and expenses, and that sum would adequately cover them. Charlotte couldn't contain her delight. Never having been more than ten miles from her parents' home in her 19 years, the prospect of a 50-mile train journey seemed like an adventure, and she would travel alone – maybe she would meet some handsome young man! She smiled at the thought; the next seven days to the interview seemed almost endless in the long hot summer of 1906.

Charlotte woke very early on 21 September, giving herself plenty of time to make the very best of herself, putting on her Sunday best dress and bonnet. Her heart was beating much faster as she approached the railway station. She offered her 10 shillings to the booking clerk and received her return ticket to Wiltham, which was the nearest station to Winstable Hall. There, according to her letter, a trap would be waiting to convey her to the Hall.

Charlotte walked slowly on to the platform and waited for her train to pull in. Soon a plume of smoke heralded its arrival and

Charlotte was held in awe as the gleaming locomotive hauled the immaculate rake of teak coaches into the station. The engine stopped alongside her and a young man with blond hair and a cheery smile jumped down.

'Hello,' he said. She smiled demurely. 'How far are you going?'

Charlotte replied that she was going to Wiltham and she had an important interview. The young man said he would tell her when to get off, then busied himself with an oilcan among the driving wheels.

Charlotte stepped into the first compartment and sat down. The station was now a hive of activity. Charlotte leaned out of the window and watched the guard's van being loaded up with milk churns, sacks of mail, and boxes of red roses. The other passengers meanwhile found their seats, then the whistle blew and the young fireman leaned over the door and handed Charlotte a single red rose. Smiling, Charlotte thanked him.

'I'm Albert,' he smiled.

It was not a long journey and as the sun was shining it was a very pleasant one. Eventually the train pulled into Wiltham and Albert leapt down and opened the carriage door, taking Charlotte's hand and helping her on to the platform.

'There we are – I hope you get the post!'

Charlotte thanked him and passed through the barrier into the station yard where a uniformed coachman was waiting with a trim little gig to take her to meet the Hon Mrs Anderson-Hunt.

Charlotte did get the position of nanny and often travelled on the same train home on her days off, always in the first compartment behind the tender and always hoping that she would see Albert, which she often did; she leaned out of the window to talk to him when the train stopped at stations.

It was over a year before Charlotte was allowed to take her charge, a little boy called Edward, home with her to meet her family on her day off. It was a very sunny day and it was made all the more complete by Albert being on duty on the return journey. He jumped down to open the carriage door for her and Charlotte and the child climbed aboard. Albert talked to them as they waited to leave. The boy had a large rubber ball that he would insist on throwing about in the compartment. Charlotte, her eyes on Albert who was taking her attention, asked him rather halfheartedly to desist, but the boy threw the ball out of the window, hitting the platform fence and rolling under the carriage.

As quick as a flash Edward darted past Charlotte and Albert and tried to look for it under the wheels. As Charlotte scrambled out of the carriage the boy was halfway under it; almost beside herself, Charlotte tried to haul him up, helped by Albert. The driver had seen the green flag and had opened the regulator to ease forward, yelling at Albert to get a move on. By this time Charlotte was halfway under the carriage herself, with Albert trying to help her. The boy had become stuck and could not get out.

The train eased forward, the driver unaware of the commotion. Charlotte screamed and the driver panicked, his hand still on the regulator. Albert leapt on to the footplate, missed his footing, grabbed the regulator to stop himself falling, and the train moved forward, dragging the nanny and child under the wheels. Nothing could save them. The wheels passed over them and life had gone.

Albert was so distressed by the whole affair that he applied for another post far away from the scene of the tragedy. But that was not the end of this sad story, nor of the nanny and child who died so horribly. Many people have seen Charlotte waiting for Albert, or her ghost, which refuses to leave that station. A curious aspect of the sightings was that people used to say that in the first compartment next to the tender there would often be the strong scent of roses.

After a while the station returned to normal. Charlotte had not been seen for some time, and Albert had been killed in the First World War, so all three participants in the awful tragedy had gone for ever – or had they?

Just before the outbreak of the second War a long passenger train was in the station taking water. The driver was oiling an axle-box when he turned round to see the trim figure of a young lady with a small boy near the first compartment of the carriage next to the tender. He made as if to talk to them when they melted before his very eyes; he could not believe it, and as the guard approached he told him what he had seen. The guard smiled.

'It's Charlotte and the boy – we've seen her on many occasions. By the way, can you smell that lovely scent of roses?'

44
The Furness Railway mystery

*I*am very grateful to Mr R. R. Mester for the following story of strange happenings on a long-abandoned stretch of the original line of the Furness Railway.

My correspondent's earliest and most vivid recollection of the haunted railway line dated from childhood memories of some 70 years ago, and referred to the short length of line between Goldmire Junction and Millwood Junction in the area of Dalton-in-Furness. Opened in 1846, this section had been early superseded and closed, and in the time of Mr Mester's childhood comprised only an overgrown formation. There were many trees and shrubs about, so visibility was rather restricted. A footpath crossed both railway and stream just below Millwood, and there was a large detached residence nearby.

'It was a creepy spot with a strong pungent smell of garlic and there was always a feeling of tension and foreboding. Frequently, and for no apparent reason, there would be a chilling burst of wind and a roar as of a passing train. In the gloaming it was possible to glimpse passing lights identical to those of a carriage in a moving train. Altogether it was an eerie experience – crossing a long-abandoned railway in the Vale of Nightshade!
Down in the Vale lay the ruins of Furness Abbey – founded by one king, Stephen, and destroyed by another, Henry VIII, at the Dissolution of the Monasteries. The roar was held by some to be that of the dispossessed and not a train at all.

My fears were shared by youthful friends, and even adult relatives at times seemed to chivvy us along as if they too expected the ghost train to rush by. Some seemed quite certain of the mystery train – one that they heard came and vanished but was never recognised.

Years later it seemed reasonable to identify the ghost train with trains on nearby well-concealed tracks linking Dalton-in-Furness with Askam-in-Furness and Barrow-in-Furness respectively, but this explanation did not entirely remove the doubts and fears experienced even in retrospect.

Maybe there was a mystery train of sorts deriving from some forgotten tale in an area served early by railways that linked with wild and remote sea shores. Whatever the explanation, for some of us there was always a sense of fear in this secluded spot, and that, moreover, linked to a train.

Perhaps it was no more than old *Coppernob*, Furness Railway No 3, built in 1846 and resident in those school days in its great glass case outside Barrow Central station, taking a turn over its old hunting grounds. . .'

45
The spirit entity

*I*have called this story 'The spirit entity' because it illustrates the fact that earthbound spirits are still very active, and making their presence felt in so many unexpected ways. I am indebted to my correspondent Mrs D. M. Ross for this compelling tale.

Mrs Ross was one of six senior citizens travelling between Glasgow and Paisley in a DMU; they were in the rear carriage with the brake unit in the centre. At Paisley signal box the train braked to a shuddering halt, and remained there for the next 30 minutes while the driver and guard proceeded to examine the underside and topside of the train. Eventually the guard climbed aboard, entered Mrs Ross's carriage and demanded to know who had pulled the communication cord, which in fact none of the passengers could see from their seated position.

When the guard was told that no one had moved from their seats, he became very worried because he said that he would have to make out a report to British Rail as to the cause of the delay. 'I'll have to put it down to person or persons unknown,' he said. In reply, one lady said, 'That would be a complete lie – have you never heard of a Spirit Entity?'

The guard agreed that the central position of the brake section prevented anyone from moving along the train without being noticed. It did not solve his problem, but the poor fellow had to make out his report and he had to find some element of evidence, and so far he had not much to write down. How the poor man finally got his report together I do not know, but I doubt that even he didn't realise that he was dealing with a supernatural force that did what it liked when it liked.

Mrs Ross tells me that she later discovered that several years earlier two trains had collided near Paisley signal box with loss of life. My informant tells me that she feels sure that the earlier event is still 'earthbound' and repeated the action. I imagine that the frustrated passengers would not be amused if they realised that the delay was caused by a restless spirit, but the report of the accident can be checked in British Rail's archives.

So that strange event and its tragic precedent may have been the work of the past or present spirit entity. . .

46
Yarwell Tunnel

*I*am very grateful to Mr H. E. Caunt, the Public Relations Officer for the preserved Nene Valley Railway in Cambridgeshire, who kindly sent me details of the strange happenings concerning Yarwell Tunnel.

During the construction of the Blisworth to Peterborough branch line of the old London & Birmingham Railway in 1845, the engineer and surveyor of the route, Robert Stephenson, being faced with hilly terrain near the villages of Yarwell and Wansford, decided to tunnel through, as a cutting was not practicable at that time.

Thus gangs of navvies (mainly Irish and living in crude huts that would only offer the most primitive shelter from the elements) were set to work on the task of excavation. Kilns were established to manufacture the bricks used to line the tunnel (approximately one million were made), the clay arriving by barges on the nearby Nene. Weekends were a particularly troublesome time; drunkenness and fighting was a real problem and special police had to be drafted in to take charge. It was reported at the time that ten or more navvies met their death fighting and falling from scaffolding, as this tunnel is unusually high and was built to accommodate double tracks.

The late Mr Walter Gilbey used to tell of many strange happenings during maintenance work in the tunnel – mysterious noises, agonising cries and sounds of men fighting. Hammers and shovels used to disappear without trace, and a newly laid stretch of track was found the following morning with all the wooden keys on the tunnel side knocked out. Sabotage was suspected, but after a thorough investigation was never proved.

On another occasion some gangers had to jump for their lives as a freight train suddenly entered the tunnel without any warning from the look-out men at either end. As soon as the train had cleared the tunnel the gangers found one of the look-out men lying unconscious by the side of the track. On being revived the man told the head ganger that he had been struck a blow on the back of the head, yet medical evidence revealed no sign of injury; moreover, his whistle, flags and lamp were never found.

Another strange happening concerns a one-time station master at Wansford station who had a pet cat called Snowy, which used to follow him everywhere. One late autumn afternoon Snowy failed to turn up for his meal, so his master went out to look for him. Unfortunately he was rather deaf and failed to hear an approaching train in the inky darkness of the tunnel – he was struck down and killed. Snowy was never seen again, yet on many occasions a greyish-white cat, unlike any of the familiar local cats, has been seen crying piteously and entering the tunnel, never to reappear.

Thus like so many railway locations, Yarwell Tunnel harbours its mysterious and macabre secrets, sharing them with some unlucky souls and leaving an indelible memory in the mind.